DEMENTIA CAREGIVING

A SELF HELP BOOK FOR DEMENTIA CAREGIVERS
OFFERING PRACTICAL COPING STRATEGIES AND
SUPPORT TO OVERCOME BURNOUT, INCREASE
AWARENESS, AND BUILD MENTAL & EMOTIONAL
RESILIENCE

JANET G CRUZ

For permissions requests, speaking inquiries, and bulk order purchase options, email: publishing@uconcept.com.

ISBN: 978-1-960188-06-9 | E-book

ISBN: 978-1-960188-07-6 | Paperback

ISBN: 978-1-960188-08-3 | Hardcover

Published by Unlimited Concepts, Coconut Creek, Florida. www.publishing.u-concept.com

Book, Editing, and Cover Design by UConceptDesigns.com

Published in the United States of America.

To All Dementia Caregivers

I dedicate this book to all of the incredible Dementia Caregivers out there who dedicate their time and energy to caring for a loved one with dementia.

I admire and appreciate all that you do! Your strength, patience, and love are an inspiration to all. Thank you for your selflessness, compassion, and dedication.

FOREWORD BY JOSE G. GARCIA, MD.

JANET G. CRUZ

THE
DEMENTIA
CAREGIVER'S
SURVIVAL GUIDE

An 11-Step Plan to Understand The Disease and How
To Cope with Financial Challenges, Patient Aggression, and
Depression Without Guilt, Overwhelm, or Burnout

CONTENTS

"Caring for a loved one with dementia takes a special kind of strength and courage."

— JANET G CRUZ

Just for you!

A Free Gift To Our Readers

- Dementia Stages cheat Sheet for Caregivers
- Tips to Identify and Cope with Emotional Triggers

https://bit.ly/bk2-bonus

INTRODUCTION

 "Caregiving often calls us to lean into love we didn't know was possible."

— Tia Walker

Being informed that someone we truly love has been diagnosed with dementia often ends up becoming one of our biggest nightmares. At that moment, you will likely get overwhelmed with uncontrollable waves of negative emotions, with the most prominent ones being shock, fear, worry, and most importantly, guilt which primarily stems from your inner voice whispering that you were negligent about taking proper care of your loved one which contributed to their dementia development.

Eventually, all of these emotions encapsulated into a whole to trigger your sense of responsibility in the most intense way, thus causing you to have this strong desire to cater to every of your loved one's needs to enable them to enjoy optimal health and functioning despite their illness. That desire, coupled with other external factors such as being the closest person to the patient, forces you to assume the role of a dementia caregiver with no experience, specialized training, or preparation.

Unfortunately, too soon into your caregiving journey, you realize the hard way that navigating the roles of a caregiver requires more than an elevated sense of responsibility. It is nothing like you had ever envisioned! On one side, you struggle with completing those different caregiving responsibilities and balancing them with other essential aspects of your life. And on the other side, you witness your loved one gradually transforming into an entirely different person, thus making it difficult for you to understand their needs and adequately cater to them.

As the challenges on these ends worsen, you begin to experience countless negative emotions and feelings that include guilt, worry, chronic burnout, anger, resentment, anxiety, depression, and pain, which are often conflicting. For instance, you worry so much about your loved one's condition. But at the same time, the chronic burnout you feel due to the overload of your caregiving duties sows seeds of resentment and frustration in your heart, thus making you get easily angry at your loved one, even at the slightest mistake. Again, at the same time, you feel guilty for getting mad at them, resenting them, or wishing they did not develop dementia and you did not have to carry so much responsibility.

Continuously going through this confusing and dizzy-like emotional cycle makes you feel worse than being in a haunted ferry wheel moving at the highest speed. And so many times, you become pushed to question everything about your decision to become the primary caregiver. Why is this caregiving journey so confusing, demanding, and emotionally draining? Or, am I the one doing something wrong? How best do I handle my loved one when they become angry, agitated, or uncooperative? Do I even have what it takes to be a great dementia caregiver?

Finding the correct answers to these disturbing questions can be frustrating, for some people around you hardly understand or have any insights about the harsh reality that an average caregiver undergoes daily. As such, you will often hear them dismiss your concerns with things like, "How bad can it be? Your father/mother/wife/husband needs you now more than ever. Thus, you must love, honor, and care for them, no matter how bad you say it is." Of course, such responses will leave you angry and frustrated, but guess what? Your prior experience of such kind will remain your last because the honest answers and solutions you genuinely seek as a primary caregiver lie within the pages of the book. But before we break down what this book will offer you, your loved one, and your overall caregiving journey, let's understand something.

Being a caregiver, especially to a loved one diagnosed with dementia, is a long and intensive journey that requires a high level of self-awareness, self-care knowledge, and many unique skills to navigate its emotional and psychological effects. For most of us, our heightened sense of responsibility and good intentions towards our dementia loved ones are the only polished and developed assets we have to offer as we take the first step into caregiving. Although these assets are essential for setting the proper foundation of your caregiving path, you need more than they to survive and succeed. Additionally, your elevated sense of responsibility to your dementia loved one could cause you to focus entirely on caring for your loved one at the expense of your physical, mental, and emotional needs. However, one of the essential lessons you must learn as a caregiver is that without adequate self-care, your caregiving roles create so many emotional and psychological effects that have the potential to crash your dreams of giving the best care and enjoying a peaceful, comfortable, and happy life with them.

To ensure that such a tragedy never occurs, you must equip yourself with adequate and comprehensive knowledge on building overall resilience and an effective self-care routine. Luckily, that crucial knowledge is part of what this book offers. It contains a practical, step-by-step approach to caring for your dementia loved one while managing yourself and caring for your mindset, resilience, and health.

In case you are still a few decisions away from starting your caregiving journey, you are in the right place. In the first section of the book, you will get to understand what it involves to take care of your dementia loved one at their early onset stage, what your caregiving roles constitute, and the critical qualities you must already have at that stage to set you up for success through your caregiving journey. As you read, you will also understand, whether practicing or about to, how your roles impact you physically, mentally, emotionally, and financially.

You probably know that dementia development occurs in stages. In case you don't, the reality is that there are seven stages that your dementia loved one will go through as the months and years pass. Each of these stages comes with unique developments, thus making your loved one require different forms of care. What works in stages 1 and 2 won't necessarily work for stages 3 and 4. Therefore, in this book, you'll learn what each stage involves, the most dominant caregiving roles in those stages, and how to handle them.

Remember those confusing and conflicting emotions, chronic burnout, and mental overload that we said your caregiving roles would inevitably push forward to you in the mid-stages of your loved one's condition? The content of this book will guide you on how to manage them through the mighty trio power of physical, mental, and emotional resilience. In building these three types of resilience, you will get introduced to several lifestyle strategies, most of which center on self-care, which you can easily incorporate into your daily routine. You will also learn practical strategies to overcome the daily challenges posed by the deteriorating state of your loved one's dementia. One such approach involves seeking help. We will break down the strategy to help understand why you should ask for help, how to ask and get a favorable response, and how to build the right caregiver support squad for your loved one.

Interestingly, most of the typical articles you find online about dementia caregiving tend to focus on how to care for a loved one in their early and mid-stages, with no sufficient information on how to offer the best care in their end-of-life phase, which can be so challenging, yet very rewarding. This book bridges that gap by providing a step-by-step analysis of what excellent end-of-life care should involve, from signing your loved one up for hospice at the right time to how you can cope safely and effectively with grief after their death.

Besides dementia end-stage care, legal and financial planning is another uncommon topic in caregiving. However, it is a powerful guarantee key to preventing you from financial bankruptcy due to your loved one's condition and ensuring that your loved one has a voice in every decision taken regarding their life, especially when they are no longer alive.

In this book's final sections, you will enjoy a simplified guide on completing financial and legal planning before your loved one loses his/her mental capacity to reason appropriately. This book will be your guidance angel, as it breaks down the function of each legal document and how to get, complete, and sign them in the U.S. By seeing how much value this book aims to offer you as a caregiver, you might wonder how I seem to know so much about the realities of dementia caregiving. Indeed! I was also a caregiver like you. I promised myself to help as many struggling caregivers as possible by sharing with them the lessons and knowledge I gained while batting the everyday caregiving struggles experienced with my loved one.

Over the years, I have helped several caregivers overcome the emotional and psychological burden of their caregiving journey. And based on my personal experiences and encounters with diverse caregivers, I realize that although a caregiver's journey inevitably comes with challenges, there are feasible means through which we can prevent those challenges from affecting us mentally, emotionally, and physically. This method involves creating an effective care plan to benefit you and your loved one.

I have designed each chapter of this book to provide comprehensive critical knowledge on creating this effective care plan. I will help you create your care plan with a step-by-step approach. Although you have never received any training or prior preparation to assume the role of a caregiver, this book is your ultimate key to unlocking the wealth of practical and cognitive knowledge that will make you an excellent caregiver.

Imagine yourself becoming a caregiver who remains calm no matter how agitated your loved one gets. Imagine being able to calm them down in seconds because you now know the right words to say and the proper ways to act. Imagine sharing a solid and close bond with your loved one, even as their cognitive functioning decline. Imagine fulfilling your loved one's wishes even when they have lost sight of who they are. Imagine being happy and at peace with yourself after your loved one's demise because you know deep within yourself that you gave them the best care without compromising your well-being. Finally, imagine how happy, fulfilled, and satisfied you will find if these highlighted imaginations transform into realities.

You deserve to enjoy such a blissful life as a caregiver. Thankfully, you are on the verge of starting a knowledge-seeking journey that will equip you with what you need to transform those imaginations into realities. So let's get started.

MAKING THE CHOICE OF BEING A CAREGIVER

> "Kindness can transform someone's dark moment with a blaze of light. You'll never know how much your caring matters."
>
> — Amy Leigh Mercree

Often time when a loved one is diagnosed with dementia, so many questions revolving around what it takes to be a caregiver pump out in our minds. The need to give the best care brings about all the questions we ask ourselves. We often wonder what it takes to be a dementia caregiver, the roles involved, how to get started, what to expect, the difficulties involved, and many more. These questions might sound unnecessary, but they are what we all think about when our loved one is first diagnosed. Getting an adequate answer to these questions, however, will help us understand, prepare, and make the bold decision of being a caregiver. This chapter will discuss all it takes to *be a great dementia caregiver.*

WHAT TO EXPECT IN THE BEGINNING

When a loved one is diagnosed with dementia from the onset, they might still show the capability of being independent. But as time goes on, as the brain degenerates, you notice that there is a need for a caregiver to step in. This is when the patients find it challenging to carry out the significant activities and duties they used to perform. They'll often need help to manage tasks like feeding, using the bathroom and toilet, drinking, taking medications, and shopping. You would also notice a feeling of anxiety, withdrawal, and depression in them.

Noting this and giving the proper care as much as it's required and as soon as possible can help reduce the symptoms of dementia. But most people, especially adults who are suffering from dementia, often hide away from it. They do this because of the fear of being judged, shame, the willingness to remain independent throughout their lifetime, or the fear of being a burden to others. But since we know this already, it becomes vital we take note of some behavior or symptoms that show that our loved one really needs help.

SYMPTOMS THAT COULD INDICATE THAT A LOVED ONE NEEDS HELP

According to a survey, about 1.5 million older ones have hidden away injuries, illnesses, and accidents from their loved ones. In addition, many older people with one specific illness, including dementia, try as much as possible to subdue the signs and symptoms of their condition.

Below are some signs and symptoms that you might notice that could indicate the presence of a dementia condition.

- Experiencing challenges in carrying out their daily activities, dressing up, toileting, drinking, shopping, etc.

- Inability to take care of their body, keeping rough hair, having an unpleasant body smell, putting on dirty clothes, having wounds and burns around the body, loss of weight, etc.

- Having extreme mood swings, loss of interest in activities they once enjoyed, and exhibiting aggressive behavior.

- Having an unkempt environment, keeping spoiled food, the smell of urine at home, and noticing damages to automobiles.

- Having difficulty completing the speech, inability to recall events, difficulty visiting places alone, and loss of reasoning ability, etc.

CARING FOR YOUR LOVED AT HOME

When you notice the symptoms discussed above after your loved ones have been diagnosed, you must start preparing a planned care routine for them. You can do this by allowing them to move to your home or you can move to theirs. In either case, the extent to which this care would be provided to them will solely depend on the stage of dementia they are in. If it's an early stage or they are only showing mild symptoms, you can stay with them for some hours a day while you take care of every other aspect of your life (education, job, marriage) for the remaining hours. On the other hand, if your loved one requires a constant care routine, then you might need to be with them almost every hour. Doing this might not be so easy to achieve. So, you can hire another individual, a nurse, caregiver, or companion who would help your loved one for hours every day while you handle other areas of your life.

If you feel you cannot afford this, consider involving Medicaid. Medicaid is a public health insurance scheme in the USA that provides support to several communities at subsidized rates. Also, involving family members in the caregiving routine would help a lot. While you are the primary caregiver, they could act as the secondary caregivers. Secondary caregivers will be able to help with several areas, including providing financial and emotional support, hiring nurses or trained caregivers, visiting healthcare centers, making provisions for medications, sorting bills, keeping medical records, doing research, and many more.

Family members sometimes do not recognize how much help you need from them as secondary caregivers until you get involved or discuss it with them. So, it will be better to have a meeting or gathering with them as soon as there is a need for caregiving. Once you have the discussion, talk about how each person would be of help and what they would do in particular. Let each person tell others what they are good at and what they would be comfortable doing. While doing this, note that some of these tasks or areas in which the family members will be helping out can be done even when they are far away from dementia loved ones, so everyone, including those staying at distant places, can be involved.

While caring for your loved one at home is good; however, there are still some options one could opt for if you can't take care of them at home. Here are the other options that could be considered:

- **Memory Care Facility for Severe, Last Stages of Dementia**

These care facilities, or homes, are structured and safe environment facilities that provide support and care for our dementia loved ones. Memory care homes have residential nurses and caregivers that take care, guide, and monitor dementia patients through their last stages of dementia.

- **Old Age Home**

Old-age homes are housing and care facilities that are meant for older people. In this home, older people are guarded and cared for by professionals. Living in an old age home could create avenues for older people to meet and have fun and enjoy basic amenities and medical facilities. But it also means they will not enjoy any personal space or choose their meals.

- **Assisted Living**

This provides the needed care and support for your dementia loved ones as long as you need them. They are homes or facilities mainly designed to meet the specific needs of people. One thing with assisted living homes is that your dementia loved one can meet other people with whom they can have fun activities while enjoying some independence. Assisted Living centers are more appropriate for earlier stages of dementia.

- **Temporary Respite for Carers**

Another option is to consider temporary care, and here, you temporarily involve trained caregiver services. It could be for a day, a few weeks, or months. And while your dementia loved one is given quality care and support during this period, you can take time to sort out other things for yourself.

THE UPS AND DOWNS OF CAREGIVING

Upside

- **Dementia Loved Ones Receive the Proper Care That's Needed**

Being a caregiver to your loved one helps ensure they receive the necessary care. You spend most of the time with them, so you know how they are coping. In most cases, you won't have to worry about the amount and quality of support and care they receive since you are there with them.

- **You are Already Conversant with Their Unique Needs**

When you assume the role of caregiver, it becomes easier to deal with your loved one's specific needs. In addition, because they are familiar with you and you understand their needs, interests, and personality, you find it relatively easier to help your dementia loved ones. Hiring a full-time caregiver or nurse will require that this professional learns about your loved ones' specific needs. Also, it might be tricky for nurses or caregivers to do their job in most cases, as your loved one could feel uncomfortable around them.

- **You Have a Chance to Strengthen the Relationship You Have with Them**

Caring for a loved one helps you build a bond with them. Even if you were close before, staying with them through this time helps strengthen your bond with them. You have an avenue to build more memories since you are spending more quality time with your loved one than ever before. Caring for someone with dementia requires an immense amount of love, and even when it seems challenging, this bond and relationship keep you going.

Downside

- **It Could Affect Family Relationships**

You must involve other family members to make the caregiving role easier for you. But while you involve them, family relationships can easily be broken if anyone cannot fulfill their role as expected. Generally, those who are committed to making a difference put forth their utmost effort in assisting. And when they achieve this, they experience feelings of resentment towards others who cannot contribute. This alone affects a family bond or relationship.

- **Finances Can Be Affected**

If you decide to be a full-time caregiver for your loved one, you might have to leave your job. Quitting your job during this period affects your finances as you get to spend more money while receiving no income. However, when you decide to work part-time while caring for your loved one in the remaining hours, you still have some income available.

- **Burnout Could Set In**

Assuming the role of a caregiver for your loved one without receiving help from other people could overwhelm or weigh you down. In addition, having to sort everything out for your loved ones deprives you of your basic needs. You will need a healthy meal, sound body rest, and exercise to keep your body and mind fit for this role you are taking. But when you cannot, coupled with the fact that you are carrying out many activities daily, burnout sets in gradually.

WHAT MAKES A GOOD CAREGIVER?

Now that we understand how you can take care of your loved ones at home and the importance of doing that, it becomes pertinent that we discuss those characteristics that make up a good caregiver. Anyone can be a caregiver, but being a good and effective caregiver comes with some distinct qualities that one must have.

- **Patience**

You must exercise patience when dealing with your dementia loved one. Dementia often comes with symptoms that slow down the response pattern of the affected one. They might often be slow when responding to your questions or even fail to respond. Sometimes, they might show aggressive or abusive behavior. As a good caregiver, you must handle the situation they put forth without getting frustrated or angry.

- **Compassion**

When you decide to be a caregiver, you must be compassionate towards them. In addition, you must be able to show empathy in the way you deal with them. If you can show these characteristics to a reasonable level, it becomes easier to relate with them, even when they exhibit unfavorable behaviors.

- **Resilience**

To be a good caregiver, you must be able to continue even when things seem so hard. Being a caregiver will not be all easy, but it is achievable. Being resilient, determined, and committed to staying with your loved one through the stages of dementia will help you achieve more. Expect to get tired at some point, but be determined to stay with them all through.

- **Attentiveness**

THE CAREGIVING role comes with quite several duties you must handle with care and attention. In some cases, you might have to manage two tasks simultaneously. As a good caregiver, you must be able to pay attention to every detail as required.

Moreover, being with dementia loved ones require that you pay attention when they give a speech, make observations of what is happening around the home, and many more. You can only achieve this when you are attentive and detail-oriented.

- **Dependability**

You will spend more time with your loved one. With this, you will know more about them ever than before. However, you will also get some information that should be kept confidential. So, to be considered a good caregiver, you must maintain the trust your loved one and other family members have in you.

Consequently, it is essential to evaluate if you have these qualities before deciding to be a caregiver. It might sometimes be challenging to choose to be a caregiver, but knowing the qualities that a good caregiver should have and assessing yourself to know if you are capable would help.

Now that you know this, it is still crucial that you understand what it entails to be a caregiver and how involved you might be when performing your roles.

- **How Involved Would You Be?**

Caregiving for a dementia loved one is like taking care of a baby. Most of the time it requires more effort, energy, and resources. If you fit in with the characteristics of a good caregiver explained above, then you are on the right track to being an *effective caregiver*. But above that, there are still some questions you should ask yourself. Giving a vivid and genuine answer to this question will help you make the best decision.

Some of the questions are:

- Can you spare some hours to care for your loved one? Or do you wish to hire a day nurse to help you for some hours?

- Where do you want to get help from? Are you willing to involve other family members?

- Are you ready to sacrifice your time for the next five to ten years?

Meditating on these questions and providing answers helps you determine if you want to be a caregiver. It also lets you choose how involved you want to be in the caregiving role. The truth is, you can decide to be a part-time caregiver for your loved one (staying with them at night and on weekends) while a hired nurse stays with them during the day. But you need to understand that signing up for this role means you will have to sacrifice your time with them for the next few years. There is no one way to know how involved you want to be. It depends on your decision and readiness to carry other family members along.

While these are enough to help you decide, know that choosing not to be a caregiver to dementia loved ones doesn't connote that you don't love them. There are several other ways you can help out. Keep in mind that choosing to be the primary caregiver could make you frustrated in the long run. You might at first do well, but as time goes on, you could easily experience burnout.

HOW TO MAKE TOUGH DECISIONS

Deciding whether to be a caregiver to your dementia loved one should be carefully done. While you must carry other family members along while deciding, be sure that no one is influencing your decision. The following pointers will help you decide on the best.

- **Get a Proper Diagnosis of the Condition**

Many other medical problems can mimic the symptoms of dementia. Eyesight problems, chest infections, hearing difficulty, kidney problems, and many more are some health conditions that mimic symptoms relating to dementia. While it is good to be on the lookout for dementia symptoms, ensure that your loved ones are adequately diagnosed by a qualified professional. If your loved one shows signs of poor spatial awareness, it would be great if you don't assume their condition as symptoms like this could sometimes result from poor eyesight. However, a proper test and diagnosis would show the real issue.

- **Create Time for An Inner Reflection**

Do not rush into making your decision. However, after going through the proper diagnosis, you must spend some time reflecting on what you want. Are you ready to get committed to this caregiving role? Do you possess what it takes to be a caregiver?

Find a quiet place where you can converse with your inner mind. Think about what you want and what you want to achieve.

- **Note Down the Pros and Cons**

When making a decision, there are usually two or more choices involved. But here, the main thing is to decide whether you will take the caregiving role or not. You should list the pros and cons of being a caregiver to your dementia loved one and then weigh or analyze the pros and cons listed. Note that while analyzing, the most important thing is to focus on the point which might have more gravity or effect in the long run. You do not have to focus on the number of points in each section. What matters most is the importance of every point you listed.

- **Set Yourself a Deadline to Decide**

Making decisions, especially the ones involving health and care might sometimes take a long time. But to be on the safer side and quicken the time you spend deciding, create a deadline for yourself. Then, within the deadline, take time to talk with your inner self, analyze what is ground, carry other family members along, and be sure to know which family member is ready to help.

- **Trust Your Gut**

After adequately analyzing all options, your inner voice will tell you what to do and make a choice. This is the process of discernment. You might sometimes feel that one choice is best for you, and at other times, you will feel it's not. If you constantly have thought about a particular option, it is best to trust your gut and make the decision.

- **Involve a Professional**

If, after the deadline, you still find it challenging to make your decision, then you might consider talking to a mental health professional like the Neurologist. They'll be able to guide you on the best decision that fits.

Being a caregiver to a dementia loved one is difficult, but achievable and worth it. While taking this role to help your loved one is great, be sure you are making the best decision that fits both of you.

THE IMPACT ON YOU AS THE PRIMARY CAREGIVER

"Regardless of what challenge you are facing right now, know that it has not come to stay. It has come to pass. During these times, do what you can with what you have, and ask for help if needed. Most importantly, never surrender. Put things in perspective. Take care of yourself. Find ways to replenish your energy, strengthen your faith, and fortify yourself from the inside out."

— Les Brown

In the previous chapter, we discussed the necessary facts to know when deciding to be a caregiver. We understood what it entails to be a caregiver and what you should expect before choosing to be a caregiver to your loved one. This chapter will discuss those impacts or changes you should expect as a caregiver. Preparing your mind and being aware of these impacts will help you work through them when you eventually begin your caregiving role. Therefore, in this chapter, you'll understand those impacts or changes that will occur to you as you begin your caregiving role. Undoubtedly, being a caregiver will affect us, but while some caregivers can manage this role, others cannot.

Before we move deeper into this, we'll discuss those roles, duties, or responsibilities associated with being a caregiver. From there, you'll get to have a broad understanding of certain factors or effects of being the caregiver.

DUTIES AND RESPONSIBILITIES YOU SHOULD EXPECT AS A CAREGIVER

As we mentioned before, it is important that you understand the specific tasks and duties you will be carrying out. Responsibilities attached to being a caregiver to dementia loved ones are many and cannot be overlooked. Knowing fully what these responsibilities are would help you prepare for the task, and more so, it will help you understand all the help you might need.

Let's now talk about each duty.

- **Evaluating Your Loved One's Medical Needs**

The caregiver will be the middleman between the patient and their medical specialist. Your responsibility is to ensure your loved one takes their medication at the right time. You also take time to observe and evaluate if there is a particular pain or changes in any part of their body. You ensure the appointments are not missed, and that you constantly contact your loved one's doctor to discuss with them how things are going. Everything that has to do with their medical well-being and health concerns you, and must be handled properly.

- **Working Out a Plan of Care**

As soon as you decide to be a caregiver, the responsibility of working out a care plan comes in. A *care plan* is a detailed note that explains the needs of your loved one and how they will be achieved. You'll list what your loved one will need, their specific needs at each stage of dementia, the number of hours of care they'll require at each stage, and many more. In addition, with a care plan, you can determine which area you want other family members and friends to visit. The care plan will help you structure what is required and how the care goals will be achieved.

- **Helping with Daily Basic Needs**

Dementia patients often suffer from mild to severe memory and mobility issues affecting various aspects of their daily life. Initially, it might seem like a dementia patient can perform daily activities like bathing, eating, dressing up, taking medication, and many more. Still, as time goes on, it might become quite difficult for them to do. In this situation, a caregiver must assist with all these activities.

- **Being a Companion to Them**

Everybody needs a companion, including your dementia loved one. Besides catering to their other needs, you will also need to make time to spend with them. A feeling of loneliness or isolation in a dementia patient could further result in depression and other health issues. To prevent this, you might sometimes need to take them for a walk and involve them in their best activities.

With this, you will strengthen the bond and connection between you both, and there'd be a much lesser chance of them feeling lonely or isolated.

- **Helping with Mobility**

You also need to help your loved one with movement. They will always need to move from one place to another daily within the home. For example, they might need to move from their bed space to somewhere in the sitting room. This could be difficult for a dementia patient to do on their own, and so it becomes necessary that you are available to help in this too.

- **Monitoring Their Feeding and Medications**

Dementia patients usually take medications that help them through the stages of the condition. You must ensure that their medicines are taken as prescribed and at the right time. Leaving your loved ones to sort out medications for themselves may be detrimental to them. To be safer, a caregiver needs to pay careful attention to this.

Apart from their medication, you must prepare and give them meals. Sorting and preparing meals for a dementia patient can be tiring, and it's a lot of work on its own because they'd most times need more nutritional food than everyone else. For this reason, one must selectively be careful when choosing the food to prepare for them and the ingredients/spices used in their food preparation. While cooking or preparing their meals is crucial, it is also important to ensure that they take the food at the right time and in the correct amount.

- **Monitoring and Assessing the Plan of Care Regularly**

As time goes on, you will need to regularly take note of the care plan. You will need to determine if there have been any changes or if there is anything that needs to be changed. While assessing, you will get to know what you've been achieving and what you've not. Consequently, you might need to talk to other family members as well, especially if they have been involved from the start. You will also need to talk to the medical specialist about the changes that have occurred or what it is needed to be attended to.

- **Preparing Transport System**

Moving dementia loved ones to places through the public transport system would not be convenient. And even if they don't intend to go to places that require a transport system, they will need to go out for medical appointments. In this case, you would be required to drive them down to the health center or get other comfortable alternatives.

- **Dealing with Behavioral Issues**

Above all, as a caregiver, it is your duty to take time to understand your loved one. They could sometimes put up different behaviors to communicate their feelings to you. You need to understand what each behavior means and what they need. You also have to manage every behavior they display, so you don't get frustrated. And, you must be prepared for some unusual behavior and be ready to deal effectively with it.

- **Shopping and Attending to Their Bills**

As you stay at home to take care of your loved one, you will always need to purchase items and go shopping. In addition, you will need to help them attend to the bills they have to pay.

- **Providing Housekeeping Role**

You will need to help keep the home clean. It can be generally difficult for the patient to keep their space intact. And, you will need to help them do dishes, keep the garden around clean, clean the floor, dispose of garbage, and do many other tasks. Keeping a home clean might sometimes be energy-draining, especially if it's a big or spacious house. However, doing it would help ensure that your loved one and yourself maintain good hygiene, while a failure to do it could pose a risk to another health issue.

With these points explained, you probably noticed that caring for a dementia patient is not as easy as it sounds, but it is achievable with the help of others. However, when these duties or roles aren't managed effectively, the impact on us becomes apparent. Many of the family caregivers we had in the past complained that caregiving duties could be so cumbersome for them. In the next section, we will look at the caregiving's impact on your overall well-being.

THE IMPACT OF CAREGIVING ON THE CAREGIVER

As we already know, assuming the role of a caregiver for your dementia loved one will greatly affect you as well. As you continue to care for them and attend to their needs daily, you would barely focus on yourself and your well-being. With little or no help from other family members, coping effectively might become unachievable. And before you know it, you start noticing the impact on your health of being a caregiver. We will now move on to discuss how caregiving may impact you.

1. You have little or no free time.

You will spend most of your time with your loved one. Because of the several duties you have to carry out, staying with them almost every time becomes necessary. If you are the primary caregiver and perform your role full-time, then having the spare time or the time to care for your own needs becomes very slim. With this comes the need to consciously manage your time effectively so you can get some rest. On the other hand, if you have a part-time nurse helping you out for some hours, you could have a little time for yourself.

2. You have less freedom of movement.

If the illness progresses, then it becomes difficult to leave dementia patients alone. Most of the time, you will need to stay with them all day, so they don't wander about or fall. When you need to get important things done, you might need to involve a relief carer for the period you won't be available.

3. You can experience a stressful living pattern.

The duties associated with being a caregiver to your loved one are many. Carrying out the duties daily could bring about a stressful life, especially if you don't involve a relief carer. In addition, the more the illness progresses, the more care is needed and the more duties you have to carry out than you used to before. While it is great to provide effective care for your dementia loved one, doing those duties every day without receiving support from other people will stress you out.

4. It could affect your relationship with other significant others.

Since caregiving for dementia loved ones involves you staying with them most of the time, it becomes quite impossible for you to focus on other significant people in your life. If you are a wife, for example, taking care of your kids and husband might be difficult. In a situation where you have to move to your dementia loved one's home, then you might unintentionally create a disconnection from your immediate family. Also, your relationship with friends might be affected as you would have little time to keep in touch or visit them.

5. You can become isolated and lonely.

If you are a full-time caregiver, then you will probably not have the time to go out to do other stuff. Going out with friends to have fun might also be difficult for you. As time passes by, you might notice a feeling of being isolated from other people and your outside world. If you are used to a socializing life, then during this period, you will have to adjust, as there would be little or no time to go out and have fun. You may even notice that your friends are gradually withdrawing from you since you barely chat with them or visit them. As a result, you might feel lonely as time goes on.

6. Your finances will be affected.

Caring for dementia loved ones requires spending money on medical and care bills, special foods and supplements, home renovations, groceries, and many more. While these are important for their well-being, raising funds for them might be difficult. If you are also the primary caregiver and stay with them full time, it even becomes more difficult as you would probably be out of a job and income. On the other hand, if you are caring for them part-time, you would have to reduce your working hours. Consequently, your finances will also be affected in this case, but you will earn some income that will allow you to cater to their needs.

7. You can experience a feeling of loss of self-identity and self-esteem.

As a full-time caregiver, you will most times spend your time with your loved one. Going out to mix and relate with other people might be difficult in this period. As such, your lifestyle begins to adjust to this demand. The resulting effect is that as time goes on, you might lose your self-identity. Even when you have to go out shopping, you would often notice that your ability to communicate or associate with other people isn't there anymore. Whether you used to be introverted or extroverted, constantly staying at home with your loved one will gradually affect your personality. You lose your self-esteem when you find it difficult to relate to this self-identity issue. Effective interaction and association with other people help us build our self-identity and self-esteem. So, failure to achieve this could affect your self-identity and esteem.

8. Your overall health and well-being might be affected.

Caring for your dementia loved one requires that you also care for yourself because you need to be healthy and strong to provide help. But in most cases, the reverse is usually the case since you barely have the time to concentrate on yourself. As a result, taking a healthy meal, going through exercise, having enough sleep, and maintaining an overall healthy lifestyle become difficult as you are overwhelmed with the urge to fulfill your loved one's needs. One thing that is common to most family dementia caregivers is the inability to get enough rest or sleep, as your loved one also needs help while you are having some rest. All of these can affect your health negatively when it is not properly looked into.

9. **You could experience burnout.**

Burnout is the most challenging effect most dementia care-givers have complained about. It simply sets in when you ignore your physical, emotional, and mental health. As you begin your caregiving role, you might become overwhelmed with how much you have to do so your loved one can be cared for. And as you carry out this role every day without taking care of your well-being, burnout gradually sets in. This is also when you easily get tired, your body demands medications and special treatment, depression sets in, and you experience several conflicting emotions every day.

10. **You can constantly have a feeling of uncertainty.**

If you are a primary and full-time caregiver, as days and years progress, you might begin to feel uncertain about your lifestyle. At first, you might feel okay and secure about how you spend your daily life, but as time goes on, you might feel uncertain about the path you are living at that moment. You could feel like the days, months, and years spent caring for your loved one could have been devoted to other things.

11. **There could be a mix of several conflicting emotions.**

Caregiving sometimes could bring about a series of emotions day in and day out. You might sometimes be so moody for no obvious reasons. On some days, your emotions might be affected by some unusual behaviors that your loved one puts up. Your loved one might sometimes be aggressive or unrespon-sive, which could make you feel unhappy. Staying with them most of the time could also make you grieve about who they were and who they are gradually becoming. You might even feel you are not doing enough to help them when you are really trying your best.

12. **You might lose interest in your best activities.**

As you spend most of your time with your dementia loved one, you make less time for the activities you like. As time progresses, you start losing interest in those activities you used to enjoy, just because you really miss those activities.

KEY TAKEAWAYS

- The roles we perform as dementia caregivers are many, and as such, we should be ready to accept as much help as we can get.

- We should consider using the service of a relief carer when needed, so we don't feel overwhelmed and stressed.

- Caring for our dementia loved one is great, but at the same time, we should be able to also care for ourselves.

- We need to be emotionally, psychologically, and physiologically healthy to provide the best care possible for our loved ones.

- While giving our best to caregiving for our loved one, we should explore several other aspects of our lives, especially the activities we enjoy. This would help us fulfill our life goals while also achieving our caregiving purpose.

You can see that caregiving for a dementia patient could greatly impact the caregiver and, despite that, they still have to provide proper care as it is required.

The best care that could be given to a loved one with dementia is the one that doesn't bring much side effect or impact on you. While many caregivers have complained about how stressful and overwhelming their role is, many caregivers still enjoy it. In upcoming chapters, you will learn how to effectively manage your caregiver role while also managing your overall well-being.

AS TIME GOES BY...

"Remember, the dementia patient is not giving you a hard time. The dementia patient is having a hard time."

— Active Pro, Nursing and HomeCare Inc.

hile there is no doubt that you will inevitably encounter most of the emotional and psychological impacts of dementia caregiving that we discussed in the previous chapter, I have great news for you! You can manage and overcome those impacts so much that you are not susceptible to burnout even as you deliver the best care to your loved one. But, how do you get to that point where you have what it takes to conquer the inescapable impacts of dementia caregiving? It all begins with understanding what your dementia loved one's condition involves. It would be best to familiarize yourself with the specific symptoms your loved one will likely showcase at the different stages of their condition as time passes. In order to be adequately prepared and reach success, you must understand what's ahead of you or what you will be facing in the caregiving journey. For this reason, our focus in this chapter centers on exploring every observable symptom in your dementia loved one that you are likely to notice as time goes by. I have classified over twenty different symptoms into two major categories: the primary and secondary symptoms of dementia.

As you probably know already, each stage of dementia has its specific symptoms, treatment options, and caregiving tasks. For example, the signs and medical and emotional needs of your loved one with stage 1 dementia would not be the same as when their condition progresses to stage 2 or 3. Thus, we will do a quick step-by-step analysis of the symptoms unique to a particular dementia level so that you can quickly and accurately identify the specific stage of your loved one's condition.

PRIMARY SYMPTOMS OF DEMENTIA

- **Memory Loss**

Memory loss is undoubtedly one of the most noticeable dementia symptoms. It is common to all types of dementia, especially Alzheimer's disease, which is the most common dementia type and accounts for an estimated 10 percent of Americans aged 65 and above (Hersh, 2018). Usually, it starts with short-term memory loss in which your loved one finds it difficult to recollect details of conversations that they recently had with other people or events in which they participated. Similarly, they might struggle to find the right words when engaging in a conversation or the name of specific things. They also tend to misplace or lose their personal belongings very quickly because they can't remember where they had previously placed them.

As time passes, the emotional aspect of their memory also gets affected. Your loved one will forget the names of people they know, including close friends and family like yourself. In addition, they tend to forget necessary appointments, or birthdays and wedding anniversaries which they typically loved celebrating. Eventually, they lose their ability to do everyday activities like cooking, driving, working, etc.

NEW PROBLEM WITH COMMUNICATION

Because of cognitive decline, dementia patients lose their language skills and struggle to find the right words to express themselves in conversations. They easily get distracted while speaking and even a slight interruption can make them lose track of what they were saying. As time goes by, their speech problems would slowly escalate to where they start to jumble up both relevant and irrelevant words in their speech. As a result, you will find it almost impossible to make meaningful sense of their utterances. In the same way, they also struggle to understand what you or other people are trying to say or mean. As such, they end up making wrong interpretations. For example, you might be making a request, and they might wrongly assume that you are trying to force them against their will.

- **Difficulty with Visual and Spatial Abilities**

As humans, our visual abilities generally involve our capacity to see clear images of people, things, and our surroundings. But beyond seeing clear visuals of these elements, we also depend on our spatial abilities to perceive correctly the sizes and exact locations of what we see. However, as the patient progresses through dementia, they gradually lose these visual-spatial abilities. For this reason, they cannot climb stairs without falling. They need help locating areas like the bathroom or kitchen around the house. Even when an object or a person is in plain sight, they might struggle to recognize elements, like traffic lights while driving. This visual-spatial decline is also responsible for making your loved one get lost or wander in familiar surroundings, making it impossible for them to locate the right path home.

DIFFICULTY WITH REASONING AND PROBLEM-SOLVING

Another significant sign of dementia is when they begin to make irrational decisions and exhibit outrageous acts consistently. For example, you can have situations where your loved one demands to go to the store at midnight or they become overly rude or flirtatious while interacting with others (Hillsboro Rehabilitation & Health Care Center, 2020).

Regarding difficulty in problem-solving, you may notice that the patient struggles to complete more complex tasks, such as settling their financial responsibilities or following recipes, or following DIY instructions. You may also observe that they need help solving complex puzzles, and they may not be as creative or innovative as you used to know them to be.

- **Problem with Planning and Organizing**

One significant brain area that dementia affects severely is the frontal lobes, which are specifically designed to enable us to efficiently plan and organize our daily activities or life actions to achieve both our short-term and long-term goals (Budson, 2018). For this reason, you might observe that your loved one, who has always been a well-organized individual, seems to have lost their planning and organization skills. They need help fixing their schedule appropriately with the fitting appointments and events. If they were fond of organizing dinners or get-togethers for the entire family, they hardly do so again. If your loved one used to be a neat freak, the unusually disorganized state of their room or the disarrangement of clothes in their wardrobe is enough to give you a signal that something is not right.

- **Difficulty with Coordination and Motor Skills**

Dementia affects your loved one's coordination and balancing abilities. You might notice suspicious changes in their style of movement. For example, they may start to walk in a prolonged and jerky manner. One might argue that sauntering is equally a common sign of aging. However, with dementia, the slowness is more intense because the body parts meant to aid your loved one's smooth movement have been overwhelmed with a high degree of muscular rigidness (Crook, 2021). In addition, your loved one may transform into an accident-prone individual who cannot help but fall whenever they try to walk a long distance or on the stairs. Although your loved one might still be able to stay steady on their feet through their condition's early and mid stages, they would surely need a walking aid when their condition becomes severe.

- **Confusion and Disorientation of Time, People, and Place**

Medical experts termed this particular symptom as *Delirium*. They further described it as a sudden mental confusion that befalls an individual and makes them unsure of where they are or what time, day, or season they are in (Dementia UK, 2020).

Studies show that one in every two dementia patients develops this condition. Thus, if you have a loved one under your care, you might notice that they constantly and repeatedly ask you questions like "What day is it? Where are we? What time is it? Who is that person?" If you also observe that your loved one keeps putting on outfits meant for the winter season during summer, then it could be a sign of delirium. Often, these symptoms of delirium can result in hallucinations wherein your loved one sees and hears things that are not present, and as such, they wrongly assume that someone with good intentions is going to harm them.

- **Changes in Personality**

Although dementia affects the brain's cognitive functioning, it often wholly transforms its victim's behaviors. Therefore, noticing your loved one consistently acting out of character could also be a significant sign of dementia development. You may see your loved one constantly exhibiting unusual repetitive behaviors like flapping their hands, fidgeting, mumbling the same word or phrase repeatedly, rocking their body, continually checking and rechecking their wallet or purse for no reason, etc. In addition, they may become more aggressive and impulsive in their actions. For example, your loved one who used to be an absolute gentleman might become foul-mouthed or openly flirty with random people.

- **Depression**

From the moment your loved one gets diagnosed with dementia, they get overwhelmed with diverse negative emotions, from fear and shock to pain and frustration over the gradual loss of their independence, which they consider a significant part of their life. Eventually, these emotions escalate into deep sadness and grief over the loss of their old selves and the dreams they had hoped to realize in their old age. In terms of depression resulting from dementia, you will realize that your loved one is slowly becoming a shadow of themselves. They withdraw from their loved ones, including you, and from all social activities. They hardly engage in conversations, no matter how much you try to get them involved in the subject of discussion. Things could get so worse that you suddenly find your loved one crying alone in the dark for reasons unknown to you and everyone else around.

- **Anxiety and Agitation**

People living with dementia are bound to exhibit intense physical aggression very often, especially when someone tries to offer them assistance or care. You might notice that your loved one is having difficulty washing dishes, and perhaps in their struggle, they break a glass. However, when you try to take over for them, they exhibit combative behaviors like kicking, biting, pushing, or pulling your hair to resist your help. If repeated consistently, such a scenario could be a significant symptom of dementia. In terms of anxiety, you might notice that your loved one is always uncomfortable when outside or in areas with large gatherings. Even within the comfort of their home, you might portray anxiety signs like repeatedly tapping their feet on the ground or biting their nails.

- **Paranoia and Delusions**

Dementia patients are often very suspicious of others because their condition makes them develop this delusional or false belief that they are being watched or plotted against by someone. Without evidence, they assume that the person in question threatens their life. An example of how your dementia loved one can exhibit paranoia or delusional signs could take this form: your mom and a neighbor had a minor argument, and the neighbor made one nasty comment about your mom. Based on that ugly comment, your mom's dementia condition could prompt her to start having wild thoughts that the neighbor hates her and wants to have her dead.

- **Restlessness and Sleep Disturbances**

Dementia causes different sleep disturbances, ranging from insomnia or excessive daytime sleeping to the inability to breathe. Against this backdrop, you might notice that your loved one takes too long to fall asleep at night. Instead, they keep rolling around on their bed restlessly. And even when they end up sleeping, it is usually for a short period before they are awake again because of fear or nightmares. They might also find it easy to sleep during the day but impossible at night.

- **Intense Mood Swings**

Have you noticed that your aged loved one cannot stop fluctuating from one intense mood to a completely different one? It could be another sign of dementia. So, for example, everybody is at the dinner table having an excellent family time, and suddenly, your grandma asks you to pass the bread, but you ignore her because you aren't ready to stand up. Then, surprisingly, your grandma gets up in anger, slams the table, and then walks up to slap you with the scariest expression on her face.

That's an example of an intense mood swing that a dementia patient could exhibit.

- **Agnosia**

People often associate agnosia with memory loss, but they are quite different with the exception that they are both significant symptoms of dementia. *Agnosia* is a neurological disorder that makes it impossible for your loved one to recognize the faces of people, objects, and smells, even when the senses responsible for those areas work perfectly. For example, your dementia loved one might have perfect eyesight, but she might not recognize your face when you stand squarely in front of her. Instead, she might have to hear your voice to identify you.

- **Audio and Visual Hallucinations**

This set of dementia symptoms has to do with your loved one claiming to see, hear, feel, or even taste things that are not in their vicinity. No matter how much you try to convince them that their claims are not genuine, they never listen because it feels natural and real to them. For example, your loved one might suddenly start screaming that bugs are crawling on their bed. Trying to convince them that there are no bugs, is just a waste of time and it might get them even more agitated.

SECONDARY SYMPTOMS OF DEMENTIA

Beyond these significant symptoms of dementia that we just examined, your loved one might also exhibit secondary signs which are not as easily noticeable as those in the primary category. Here are some of those symptoms.

- **Listlessness and Apathy:** They tend to have zero enthusiasm or interest in any activity that others in their age group might have fun doing or have been equally used to love before. They would rather sit down and watch others than participate.

- **Alcohol and Drug Use:** Remember, we mentioned depression as one of the primary symptoms of dementia. To escape that intense sadness and grief, your loved one might resort to consuming unhealthy amounts of alcohol or drugs, which will offer them temporary ecstasy.

- **Emotional Distress Resulting in Physical or Verbal Outbursts:** Although dementia tends to be majorly characterized by physical pain, that pain can destabilize the emotional state of your loved one and intensify their negative emotions, such as anger and frustration. As a result, you might notice that your loved one, who used to be a sweet, gentle soul, is suddenly guilty of yelling, verbally abusing people, throwing and breaking things, and attempting to attack others physically.

- **Loss of Initiative:** If your loved one has always had the characteristics of a charismatic leader and suddenly starts depending on others to take the lead before they take action, it could be a sign that they have dementia. The damage that this disease causes to the frontal lobes of the brain makes them lose interest in almost every activity and struggle to get going independently without encouragement or gentle prompts from someone they trust (Social Care Institute For Excellence, 2018).

- **Poor or Declined Judgment:** Since dementia negatively impacts the reasoning and thinking ability of your loved one, they are bound to develop a poor sense of determination. As such, you cannot trust your dementia loved one to make effective decisions regarding critical aspects of their lives, especially with their finances and safety. Earlier, we gave the example of a dementia patient asking to go to the grocery store at midnight; that example is equally a clear exhibition of poor judgment.

PROVIDE THE BEST SUPPORT AT EACH OF THE SEVEN STAGES OF DEMENTIA

In the early days of our caregiving journey, many of us often fail to understand that, regardless of the dementia type, your loved one's dementia condition does not evolve into its worst form within a couple of days, weeks, or even months. You might not believe it is, but the timeframe concerning dementia development is usually a matter of years.

Dementia is a special kind of syndrome in which the cognitive damage to the patient's brain cells progresses from one stage to another as time passes. You will recall that we mentioned earlier that medical specialists and scientists had identified only seven significant stages through which a dementia patient's progression of cognitive decline evolves.

In my previous book: *The Dementia Caregiver's Survival Guide: An 11-Step Plan to Understand the Disease and How to Cope with Financial Challenges, Patient Aggression, and Depression Without*

Guilt, Overwhelm, or Burnout, we equally examined some crucial details relating to the symptoms that come with each dementia stage. However, this chapter will explore this topic from another significant perspective. We will emphasize how long each stage should last, the likely needs of your loved one, and the best support you as a caregiver should offer at each of the seven dementia stages. Let's begin!

- **Stage 1: No Memory Deficit**

No matter how observable you might be, there is little to no chance that you can single-handedly make an accurate dementia diagnosis at this stage. And this inability has nothing to do with you. In contrast, it is how dementia works at its very first stage. Although the disease is already present in your loved one's brain and is undoubtedly creating massive damage to its cells, it does not showcase any visible symptoms like memory deterioration or any signs we examined in the previous section. As such, you tend to see your loved one navigate their daily life activities with ease, faultless memory skills, and outstanding independence.

Depending on the type of dementia involved, the timeframe for the completion of the first dementia stage usually ranges from a few months to a significant number of years. It could be five, ten, or twenty years, as with Alzheimer's disease, which we already know as the most common dementia type. But despite the non-visibility of your loved one's dementia symptoms, as a caregiver, you cannot afford to watch silently and wait until those signs showcase themselves. You can do much now, especially if you already know of a recurrent history or high genetic risk factor of developing a specific dementia type in your family. In such situations, is it best to get your loved one to do a *Positron*

Emission Tomography (PET) scan? Unlike other common types of scans, a PET scan has proven to be very effective in helping medical professionals identify essential changes in specific body parts, which serves as clues that a progressive disease like dementia is discreetly developing. By getting an early dementia diagnosis through a PET scan, you can help ensure that the progression of your loved one's cognitive decline is slowed or delayed for as long as possible.

- **Stage 2: Slight Cognitive Decline**

This stage of dementia is also known as *age-associated memory impairment*. This name stems from the fact that at the second stage of dementia, the cognitive damage to your loved one's brain cells has slightly worsened. As a result, they begin to exhibit subtle symptoms, primarily focusing on memory impairment. You will see them showcasing minor signs of memory loss, like quickly forgetting the locations of their personal belongings, misplacing little things like their car keys, or not remembering familiar names of people or their scheduled appointments. Nonetheless, these memory loss symptoms hardly create a harmful interference in their daily lives because they often end up remembering whatever it is that they might have forgotten.

Without any prior understanding of what dementia involves, you, as a loved one to a person with stage 2 dementia, would most likely dismiss those symptoms as signs of aging. So, when your dad constantly forgets his car keys' location, you make fun of him saying, "Oh, pops! You are getting old." However, just for confirmation, it is best to encourage your loved one to get a PET scan for dementia.

In addition, you can help improve their memory skills by creating specific but easy-to-find spots for objects that your loved one often misplaces and labeling those spots so that your loved one never misses them when looking for something.

- **Stage 3: Mild Cognitive Impairment**

At this stage, you do not need a medical examination to suspect that your loved one has dementia, for the symptoms become more apparent. In terms of their memory impairment symptoms, you notice it becomes more frequent and they no longer control it. So while in the previous stage, they take less time to remember things they appear to forget, you will observe that your loved one now takes much longer to remember. They often need someone else to help them with a clue to remember certain things. These signs of memory impairment are still mild because they do not affect the critical aspects of your loved one's daily lifestyle; they can live independent lives. However, their concentration levels get severely affected. They take longer to complete complex tasks, and their productivity level in their workplace could be affected.

Experts have concluded that this stage takes 2 to 5 years to complete and progress into the next stage. But guess what? As a caregiver, you have the chance to stall that progression for as long as possible. You can do this by convincing your loved one to get a definitive diagnosis. You can then develop an effective care plan for your loved one with the recommendation of a healthcare expert. For example, if your loved one has a tedious occupation, it would be best to convince them to quit, or you can find a less stress-prone job. In addition, you should increase the number of times you check in on them and make yourself more available.

In addition, this stage is the best time to create a stable routine plan for your loved one and encourage them to stick to it. You can make a timetable that showcases when and how your loved one can perform different basic activities, be it bathing, grooming, dressing, eating, taking medication, etc. By making them follow this timetable consistently, you are indirectly helping your loved one store that systematic life routine in their long-term memory. Thus, even when their memory deteriorates to its worst level, they can still predict their daily activities with little to no help.

- **Stage 4: Moderate Cognitive Decline**

Stage four marks the onset of the mid-stage dementia crisis, in which the patient gradually loses their capacity to live an independent lifestyle. Of course, as you might have already predicted, memory impairment worsens such that your loved one cannot readily recall personal information about themselves, like their birthdays, the high school or college they attended, childhood memories, and so on. But more than memory impairment, stage 4 dementia affects the cognitive ability of your loved one. Hence, they often need help to complete complex or multiple steps like driving, paying bills, cooking meals with complicated recipes, using electronic appliances, etc. Their sense of reasoning also suffers some degree of impairment. For example, you might notice your loved one constantly giving unrelated answers to questions or making irrelevant contributions during discussions.

Although you might consider it a bit early, your loved one needs to have someone who can be available when they need help with the previously mentioned complex tasks and take care of their medical needs. This person could be you or other family members the patient trusts. You should also gently convince them to quit driving and offer to permanently take over their financial obligations so they do not get duped. It is, however, essential to note that your loved one is slowly getting overwhelmed with anxiety and agitation. As such, you must handle them with as much love, care, and patience as possible. Don't decide on their behalf, but focus on making them see what you want and what's best for them.

- **Stage 5: Moderate Dementia**

At the stage of moderate dementia, the memory impairment and cognitive decline of your loved one hit a point that is just a little above rock bottom. Although they might still complete their basic routine activities with little to no help, they inevitably lose a significant part of their cognitive functioning abilities, especially their orientation of time, place, and even people. You will notice that your loved one cannot tell what day, month, or season it is, no matter how much you remind them. They often end up picking the wrong outfits to wear for specific occasions. They also frequently get lost in familiar environments because they suddenly cannot recall what route to take. Consequently, this inability to correctly tell time and place, and their inability to remember important things and provide reasonable answers or contributions, leaves your loved one frustrated.

As a result, you see a drastic change in their personality. They become more secluded, quiet, antisocial, easily irritated, and violent. Trying to offer support at this point will be much more complicated than in previous stages. First, however, you must never forget that your loved one is overwhelmed by the fear of what this disease could do to them. They also feel immense frustration and a sense of loss that a significant piece of their life disappears daily. For those reasons, you must involve your loved one in every care plan you make to support them. If they are experiencing disorientation and cannot seem to pick out the right outfits, you can offer to help them without making them feel that they have lost their independence.

You can also improve their memory by encouraging them to tell stories about themselves. While some of these stories would reflect your loved one's unrealistic imagination, you will discover some truth proving that they still have knowledge of specific life memories in their brains.

- **Stage 6: Severe Cognitive Decline**

This stage marks the onset of the most critical dementia state. Your loved one loses the little independent capacity to complete routine and basic activities like bathing, grooming, or feeding alone. Thus, you must be available to care for their every need. It is no longer feasible for them to live alone and independently at this stage. You must probably be with them to provide 24/7 support and care.

Your dementia loved one would also experience a lesser degree of mobility, coordination, and balance difficulty. In addition, the rigidness in their muscles is so intense and painful that they need extra support to move from one place to another. Also, the changes in their personality become more severe, for they start exhibiting symptoms of intense aggressiveness, hallucinations, or paranoia that you are out to harm them.

Finally, because they can no longer recognize your name or face, even as a closed loved one, it becomes more difficult for you and other family members to help them.

In spite of all these, you need to remain as calm and patient as possible with them. Your calmness can go a long way in helping them to cool down when they are going through terrible melt-downs. Then you can take advantage of such a moment to bond with your loved one by reading to them, playing fun games, or simply reminiscing over old photos.

According to medical experts, stage 6 dementia lasts about one to two years. Sadly, most patients rarely survive this stage because their immune system weakens as they are more suscep-tible to severe infections like pneumonia. Thus, to prolong the lifespan and improve the health of your loved one, you have the ultimate responsibility as the primary caregiver to make sure that they attend every medical appointment, take their medica-tions when due, and stick to their healthcare provider's instructions.

- **Stage 7: Severe Dementia**

Unsurprisingly, this stage is the most critical state of any dementia patient. When your loved one reaches this point, they will have lost total control over their cognitive functioning and overall body management. They find it almost impossible to talk; every utterance tends to be incoherent. They also struggle with eating and drinking. Soft meals are the only things they can eat and swallow. Their violent meltdowns and delusional moments become more frequent and uncontrollable. Conse-quently, your services, support, and love as their caregiver become insufficient; and instead, a greater need for appropriate professional help arises. You and the entire family must choose the best professional care service to manage your loved one's condition more efficiently, especially their medical needs. For example, you could get them to a nursing home or hire the services of a full-time live-in nurse or a professionally trained caregiver.

Before we wrap up this chapter, I had prepared a chart you can download that can help you understand the specific caregiving tasks required at every stage of dementia. You can download the *Dementia Stages Cheat Sheet for Caregivers* from the QR code at the end of this chapter.

Of course, the tasks highlighted in these charts are demanding and burdensome. As such, it is relatively easy to bury yourself in these never-ending caregiving tasks. However, you must fight against that urge to forget your needs and self-care, because failing to do so would surely make you more susceptible to chronic stress and burnout. Luckily, we'll learn about the signs of stress and burnout you should watch out for as a caregiver and how to manage and overcome them effectively.

BONUS DOWNLOAD: DEMENTIA STAGES FOR CAREGIVERS CHEAT SHEET

WATCH OUT!

"Being deeply loved by someone gives you strength while loving someone deeply gives you courage."

— Lao Tzu

ased on the caregiving tasks we analyzed in the previous chapter, you will agree that dementia caregiving demands that you dedicate a tremendous amount of time, money, and energy to your loved one's care, no matter the stage of their dementia condition. However, in delivering those unpaid but rewarding services, we must watch out not to become a victim of caregiver stress syndrome or burnout.

One major misconception we as primary caregivers tend to have, is that we must focus on supporting and assisting our loved ones at the expense of our own personal needs. When you start thinking of yourself, you quickly caution your inner self, saying, "Oh no! I'm being selfish! My dad/mom needs me more! I shouldn't be thinking about myself right now." Because of such thoughts, you are forced to neglect your needs. And without realizing it, you keep going without giving yourself a break or getting the much-needed help from other family members and friends. Instead, you firmly believe you don't need any assistance at all and have what it takes to handle it alone.

Eventually, your neglect of self-care and refusal to seek external assistance causes you to experience *caregiver stress syndrome* or *burnout* in its full force. With no delay, this condition often weighs down on your physical and emotional being so severe that it snatches away your capacity to achieve what has always been your top priority: to take the best care of your dementia loved one. But, of course, no dementia caregiver ever wants to succumb to such a low point. Hence, to ensure you never reach that point in your caregiving journey, let's begin this chapter by exploring the warning signs that explicitly showcase that you need external help. Some of these signs also include physical and emotional problems to confirm that you suffer from caregiver stress or burnout and equally need help.

16 Signs that You Need Help as a Dementia Caregiver:

1. You mostly feel guilt and resentment.

Guilt and resentment are contradictory emotions that become more intense and pronounced when a caregiver is stressed out or at burnout. The harsh truth about every caregiver's journey is that although you genuinely love that person under your care, your decision to become their caregiver doesn't solely stem from love but more out of obligation or perhaps guilt. You feel deeply responsible for your loved one, so you might assume their dementia diagnosis is partially your fault. You think, "If I have been more available to care for my mum/dad, perhaps they would not have developed dementia."

These guilt feelings make you set unrealistic expectations regarding caring for your loved one's needs. But despite the level you push yourself to care for them, you still feel you are not doing enough. Eventually, resentment develops, especially when your efforts are hardly appreciated or acknowledged. You constantly think, "Why me?" Despite your love and compassion for your loved one, you cannot help but resent them for taking away your peace of mind, time, freedom to live as you wish, and perhaps your job. Of course, you will still feel guilty for having these resentful thoughts, but you can hardly stop them from invading your mind. Ultimately, when things get to this point, it is a clear sign for you to step back, readjust your caregiving situation and create room for the appropriate help.

2. You feel constantly worried.

As a dementia caregiver, it is pretty standard for you to get worried about your loved one's condition, especially when you are not with them. However, that weariness becomes problematic when you still cannot relax even when your loved one is well-catered for and has all they need to be happy and healthy. For example, your brother decides to handle your caregiving roles for a day so that you can take a break. However, every minute that you are away from your dementia loved one, you cannot help but worry. You keep calling your brother to ask if your loved one is okay, to where it gets very annoying to the other party. When you experience such a degree of weariness, you must seek professional help, especially regarding your emotional and physiological well-being.

3. You feel uncomfortable asking for help.

This point is perhaps one of the most ironic facts about dementia caregiving. So often we feel uncomfortable asking for help from those who have what it takes to improve our lives and those of our loved ones. This discomfort stems from our fear of being mocked, pitied, or treated in a demeaning way by those from whom we seek help. In other cases, maybe we firmly believe that we can handle every task with no one else's help. However, such assumptions are entirely false and could serve as stumbling blocks to your goal of giving the best care possible to your loved one. Thus, that feeling of not being comfortable is an ironic sign that you genuinely need to seek help, both for yourself and your dementia loved one, as fast as you can.

4. You have no time even for research into the problems.

At the beginning of the last chapter, we emphasized that the first step to overcoming the inevitable challenges in your caregiving journey lies in getting adequate knowledge about your loved one's condition. There is so much you have to learn about the syndrome. However, you might be in a situation where you have little to no time to gain such essential knowledge because you are too busy juggling your job with taking care of your dementia loved one's needs. In such a situation, it becomes paramount to get help.

5. You don't know what your resources are.

Lack of resources is another factor that could deter you from learning as much as you should concerning your loved one's dementia condition. In such scenarios, it is also necessary to consult health providers, friends, and family members to help yourself with the appropriate dementia resources to look out for and where to find them.

6. You can't afford to get outside help.

As we mentioned before, having a dementia loved one under your care comes with a high financial burden that some of us often cannot satisfy on our own. For example, in the previous chapter, we learned that when your loved one's dementia progresses from one stage to another, it requires more intensive and adequate medical care as often as possible. However, the healthcare providers can only administer this medical care after you have settled expensive bills, which are usually too much for a single person to handle. Thus, when your loved one's condition reaches such stages, the best and safest option is to seek help.

7. You are stuck at home all day with no transportation or time.

Dementia caregiving is undoubtedly one of the loneliest jobs in the world, especially if your loved one's condition is at the mid or critical stages, which requires round-the-clock care. However, needing external help becomes paramount when you find yourself stuck at home all day, taking care of your loved one's needs and rejecting every invitation to social events or hangouts sent to you. It even becomes arduous to go to a place as essential as the grocery store. Going out with your dementia loved one using public transportation is undoubtedly burdensome. Thus, getting someone with a private car to help you both in terms of transportation becomes crucial.

8. You live too far from any outside help.

In the last chapter, we emphasized that as your loved one progresses through the stages of dementia, it becomes much easier for them to get lost or wander. For such a situation, you and your loved one must live where other people, like neighbors, can help monitor your loved one's movement when you are unavailable especially when you live too far away or in pretty lonely surroundings. Similarly, suppose you both live far from essential facilities like hospitals and grocery stores. In that case, it is another sign that you need help with transportation and accessibility.

9. **You are always tired and only sleep when you get a break.**

You may experience high fatigue and insomnia, especially when at burnout. Your body feels weakened and drained of energy throughout the day because you cannot sleep well at night and constantly struggle with nightmares. As such, you cannot help but take breaks between delivering your caregiving roles. Those breaks serve as nap times that help relinquish your energy so you can still care for your loved one. However, a caregiver in a state of severe tiredness could cause more harm than good to the patient under their care.

10. **You are gaining or losing a lot of weight.**

Suppose you are experiencing unexplainable weight changes. In that case, there is an excellent possibility that the *caregiver stress* or *burnout syndrome* is taking over your body, and you need help. So, what's the connection between this syndrome and weight gain or weight loss? If you have read my book, *The Dementia Caregiver's Survival Guide*, you probably remember that when your body is constantly in a highly stressful state, it produces the stress hormone *cortisol* in significant and potentially dangerous amounts. This increase in cortisol production automatically leads to a decline in your body's sugar level. And because your body wants to increase that declining sugar level, it makes you crave more sugary and fatty foods. Thus, you find yourself eating so much of such foods because it gives your body immense pleasure and comfort. In no time, you notice you are adding extra pounds of weight at an alarming rate.

Weight loss can also be attributable to high levels of stress. When you are feeling stressed and overwhelmed, you think it helps you to be ready, responsive, and proactive in meeting the needs of your loved one. However, the persistent activation of this "flight and flee" response interferes negatively with your digestion process, leaving you with a poor appetite. Thus, you could take care of your loved one's needs for hours without feeling the need to eat. And even when you do, the number of meals will be lesser, and you need more essential nutrients.

11. **You are more easily angered and irritable and lose your temper.**

You honestly and wholeheartedly love that person under your care. However, when the *caregiver's stress* sets in, it puts your mind in such a chaotic state that it becomes difficult for you to showcase that love. You quickly get irritated and angry if your loved one commits even the slightest mistake or showcases minor uncooperative behaviors. Mind you, you overlooked such behavior in the past without even thinking twice. But because the stress syndrome makes it hard to control your temper, you tend to get into more arguments with your loved one. You yell at the patient more often. And whenever the patient has those aggressive meltdown moments, your unconscious response is to attack in the same way he/she is doing to you, rather than trying to calm down the patient. However, the patient is not the only one who suffers from this aftermath of caregiver stress syndrome; your friends and family also do. For no reason, you may get into arguments or fight with your friends and other people who are most dear to you. When such situations begin to occur, especially when it happens frequently, then there is no doubt that you need help.

12. **You feel sad and hopeless.**

Suffering from caregiver stress syndrome and burnout is a significant instigator of depression in dementia caregivers, demanding you to scream for help. Depression makes you experience an intense and persistent feeling of sadness and hopelessness. You feel sad because you believe you are the world's unluckiest person whose life is not worth living. You grieve for yourself, your loved one, and the dreams you both will have to forgo and forget because of one dementia diagnosis.

No matter how much you try to be happy, your inner voice keeps telling you that your loved one will eventually die, leaving you alone in this "miserable" world. So, you often think, "What's the point of my life? Why can I not be like my friends living their best lives? Why am I and my loved one so unlucky?" And the more you keep having such thoughts, the more the idea of committing suicide gains momentum in your mind. The moment you ask yourself, "Wouldn't the world be a better place without me in it?", you know that you have reached the peak of your burnout phase and *seriously* need professional help.

13. You have lost interest in things you used to enjoy.

Your persistent sadness and hopelessness make it impossible for you to derive pleasure or satisfaction from activities you used to enjoy as hobbies. Even when you try to rekindle your enthusiasm for these activities, your mind gets plagued with guilt for having fun. You cannot help but think about your loved one in pain. You also have these sad assumptions that you no longer fit in with your friends or that other people see you differently now. Because you do not want to awaken those terrible feelings, you would much rather avoid any activities that remind you of how "perfect" and "uncomplicated" your life used to be before your loved one's dementia diagnosis.

14. **You are turning to alcohol or drugs, including prescription medications.** Based on our discussion in the last chapter and the last 15 signs analyzed so far, we can agree that the physical and emotional burden of dementia caregiving is overwhelming. At the burnout stage, it becomes so much that you might get forced to turn to consuming unhealthy amounts of alcohol or abusing other substances to numb your physical and emotional pain.

The likes of marijuana or stronger narcotic drugs are not the drug types a person can misuse. You could unconsciously abuse prescription drugs like painkillers, anti-anxiety medications, sleeping pills, stimulants, etc. By consuming such substances, you will feel high or drowsy, which gives you a temporary and false escape from your reality. The need for more of that escape can make you get addicted to them. To avoid such consequences, you need to take a step back from caregiving and get help the very moment you notice you are turning to alcohol or any other substance for relief.

15. **You have frequent aches and pains, or illnesses.**

When you begin to approach the phase of burnout, your brain and body muscles tend to get strained so much that it leads to immense pain. Because you are constantly multitasking and obsessing over your loved one's needs, the mental overload in your brain gets worse, and you start experiencing headaches more frequently than usual.

The caregiver stress syndrome makes you feel aches in different parts of your body, especially those muscle areas that you most utilize when delivering your caregiving duties. At first, it might seem like regular body aches. However, you'll notice that it becomes more intense, for you begin to experience symptoms like painful muscle stiffness or spasms, mobility problems or balance and coordination problems, etc. In the worst cases, your ability to walk normally could be severely affected.

16. **Your health needs medical attention.**

The caregiver stress syndrome causes frequent aches by over-taking your body, and awakens your preexisting medical conditions, especially if such situations are aggravated by persistent stress. For example, studies have shown that dementia caregivers experience the severity of health conditions such as high blood pressure, type 2 diabetes, obesity, hypertension, and other cardiovascular diseases because of the stressful nature of the job. However, dementia caregivers with preexisting medical conditions are not the only ones at a disadvantage when they develop caregiver stress syndrome. Research studies have proven that caregivers with no underlying medical conditions are also susceptible to specific ailments due to their caregiving jobs' physical, physiological, and emotional burden.

Let's look at some of the common caregiver ailments specifically mentioned by medical experts.

- Breathing problems such as asthma and emphysema

- Diarrhea or constipation

- Body aches

- Flu and common cold

- An increase in blood pressure, which is a cause of strokes or heart attacks

- Type-2 diabetes

- Menstrual cycle interference. Suppose you are already in the stage of menopause. In that case, there is a high possibility that your role as a dementia caregiver could intensify or complicate the physical symptoms of menopause, such as hair thinning, sore breasts, painful joints, increased urination, and susceptibility to urinary tract infections, insomnia, etc. (Pieyrangelo, 2020).

These ailments listed above are powerful predictors that show-case that you are experiencing poor health. But more impor-tantly, they signal your need to step aside for a short period to care for your medical condition adequately in order to better care for your loved one's needs. Ultimately, seeking appropriate help for yourself is as important as getting help for your dementia loved one's care.

Having understood the signs that can enable you to figure out whether you need help or have been overwhelmed with care-giver stress syndrome, the next question is: How do you over-come this condition and its negative effects? To answer this question in a more elaborate yet satisfying way, let's check out the most effective steps to lessen or ease the physical and emotional effects of caregiver stress syndrome.

STEPS TO LESSEN OR EASE THE PHYSICAL AND EMOTIONAL EFFECTS OF THE CAREGIVER STRESS SYNDROME OR BURNOUT

1. Make self-care part of your daily routine.

Most of us think of self-care as activities such as going for a body massage or manicure, taking long and luxurious vacations, etc. Against this backdrop, we quickly dismiss the idea of self-care because it is time-consuming and expensive. But guess what? The best and most effective self-care routines are hardly complicated, time-consuming, or expensive. It's simply about knowing yourself and consistently adopting habits that nurture your health and happiness.

There are several effective self-care habits you can incorporate into your daily routine, which will improve your lifestyle and well-being as a dementia caregiver. And it all begins with you creating a morning routine that can keep you motivated and energized throughout the day. These morning routines could include mind-calming activities like taking a cup of your favorite coffee or tea, meditation, exercising, journaling, taking a walk to enjoy the morning breeze, or even reciting affirmations. It could be any activity; most importantly, it effectively decluttered your mind and prepared you well for day one. The same applies to your night or bedtime routine. Based on what we have learned so far, you learned that sleep is a crucial necessity for every dementia caregiver. After spending most of your day caring for your loved one, you deserve a restful and calm evening. You can take up simple activities like reading a novel or watching your favorite movie to relax your brain and prepare your body for proper sleep.

In making self-care a part of your daily routine, you must also focus on the little things that make you happy. Do things that make you comfortable as you go through your day. It could be as simple as throwing jokes with your loved one, dancing around the house, organizing family get-togethers, etc.

Ultimately, an essential quality of having a self-care plan is *consistency*. Ensure that you remain consistent as much as you can. There are several ways you can do this. It could be by getting an accountability partner or someone to do some of these activities with you. Or you create a tracker to record your progress. The more progress you see, the more motivated you will get. Overall, it would be great if you reward yourself after realizing that you have maintained consistency for a set period.

2. **Keep things simple - defer, delegate, drop.**

Get clear on what is important and focus on it. The dementia caregiver's list of roles and tasks is never-ending as there is so much to do and complete over 24 hours. Thus, to cut any chance of developing caregiver stress or reaching the stage of burnout, you need first to step back and reassess your situation, you can make a detailed note of every caregiving task you have to complete, whether daily, weekly, or monthly. Then you sort those listed roles in order of importance to improving your loved one's well-being.

Once you have derived that critical information, it is time to pick out the tasks you are in the best position or have the best physical, emotional, and psychological capability to perform. For example, you are that one family member your loved one trusts the most. Because of that trust, they allow only you to help them take their baths, dress up, cook, and do other essential activities. That special bond you share with your loved one automatically makes you the best person for the caregiving role. Any other person attempting to take up that role may suffer aggressive rejection from your loved one. So, what happens to the remaining significant tasks and roles that you have listed on that note? It's straightforward - you outsource them as much as possible to other organizations and people like friends, family, church members, or neighbors whom you trust and know are better positioned to help your loved one's condition. For example, you are struggling to pay your loved one's medical bills. Because you lack the financial capacity, your best option is to reach out to people or local dementia-support organizations that can provide you with financial aid, whether in cash or kind.

As much as we would not want to admit it, this step is often too difficult because of our pride. However, for the loved one under your care, you must learn to lose that pride and ask for help when necessary. By outsourcing these tasks to the right people and getting help where and when required, you can find more time to practice your self-care routine and relax your soul, body, and mind in the best way possible.

You may still wonder how to figure out the best time to outsource and take a break from your caregiving roles. In that case, you don't have to search further. All you have to do is take a few steps back and review each of the 16 signs we analyzed in this book's first part. Then, once you notice you are experiencing any of those signs, consider it the best time to outsource and take a break!

3. **Find the best ways to release and process intense emotions so they don't build up and fester.**

In most cases, before dementia caregivers begin to lose control of their emotions, especially in anger and frustration, they tend to have pent down countless moments of guilt, anger, and frustration over the long run until they unconsciously reach their limit. Consequently, your ideal course of action for preventing such intense emotions from arising is to identify the most effective methods for dealing with and releasing these emotions as they arise. One of such most effective ways is getting a mentor, confidante, or accountability partner who truly understands how emotionally and physically demanding your dementia caregiving job is. They should also be people who know you in ways others don't.

Having such people at your disposal means that you can visit them as frequently as possible to pour out what you truly feel about your job and your dementia loved one. Of course, pouring those thoughts and emotions tends to bring a deep sense of relief, but that's only the tip of the iceberg regarding the benefits of such people. Since your mentor is well-versed or experienced in dementia caregiving, they serve not only as good listeners but can also provide you with insightful advice to truly understand what you are experiencing and how you can overcome those emotions and take better care of yourself and your loved one.

Even when you don't come to them, a good confidante monitors your activity and pulls close to the patient when they realize you are struggling and need their help. In Chapter 6, we'll explore more effective ways you can process and let go of intense emotions like anger, guilt, irritation, or frustration.

4. **Focus on doing things that help you and your dementia loved one feel good.**

While explaining how you can incorporate self-care into your daily routine, we emphasized that the activities that make up your self-care plan have to be things from which you derive great pleasure and satisfaction. Similarly, when creating a stronger bond of joy and happiness between yourself and your loved one, you must focus on activities fulfilling this same criterion. In addition, you know this patient better than anyone else. Hence, even though your loved one might not tell you exactly what they want to do, you can use your knowledge to choose for them.

Mind you, there has to be a balance in that you must also pick out activities that are equally pleasurable. So it's about your loved one and your personal enjoyment. There is a long list of activities from which you can choose. For example, you could start going outdoors more often. You could organize an outdoor picnic with just yourself and your loved one or other close family members to laugh and reminisce about old fun memories. Playing fun and silly games like Monopoly, Ludo, puzzles, etc., could also be effective. You can also go to the beach or pool to swim with your loved one, splash in the water, and walk by the ocean. Fun exercises like yoga, dancing, or stretching are also excellent choices. Ultimately, when choosing the appropriate fun activities to relieve yourself from symptoms of caregiver stress syndrome while equally making your loved one happy, all you should think about is, "What do I enjoy doing the most? What makes me happy?" You will indeed find the best answers!

Before we wrap up this chapter, there is one more unfinished business that we have to handle, and it's a significant physiological symptom that you should watch out for to confirm that you are under the captivity of the caregiver stress syndrome or burnout. It's known as *Caregiver PTSD*!

- **Caregiver or Carer PTSD**

Studies have shown that one in every five dementia caregivers develops this mental condition, especially when caring for their loved one for an extended period (Dementia. Org, 2013). So, how does this *Caregiver PTSD* develop?

Like any other type of PTSD, *Caregiver PTSD* stems from the traumatic psychological distress that you constantly experience as you care for your loved one. For example, when you keep seeing your loved one, whom you have known for your entire life, gradually transform into somebody you barely recognize, you feel a sense of grief that feels like you are watching them drifting slowly from you and the rest of the world. That sense of despair causes your psychological distress and creates havoc in your physical and emotional well-being, ultimately leading to *Caregiver PTSD*.

Its significant symptoms include anxiety, depression, confusion, guilt, inability to control emotions, emotional detachment from the rest of the family and friends, flashbacks or nightmares of your loved one's violent meltdown moments, etc. If you take a second look at the symptoms we listed, you will see significant similarities between them and the 16 signs we examined in this chapter's first part. So what does that tell you? It's possible to overcome *Caregiver's PTSD*, and the four comprehensive steps we analyzed for overcoming caregiver stress syndrome and burnout are a great way to get started.

Besides the different signs of caregiver stress syndrome, we have examined in this chapter, there are several other resources you can take advantage of to confirm if you genuinely suffer from caregiver stress syndrome. These resources include standard-ized questionnaires, quizzes, and checklists designed by medical experts and psychologists to help you assess or measure the level of your stress and burnout (American Psychology Association, 2020). Some resources include:

- The Alzheimer's Society of Canada's Caregiver Stress Assessment Checklist

- The American Psychological Association's Caregiver Self-Assessment Questionnaire

- The AARP's Caregiver Stress Quiz

Each of these highlighted resources is easily accessible online. So all you have to do is type these names into the search engine's search box, which will direct you to the websites where you can assess these quizzes or questionnaires.

As a primary caregiver, you must understand that your mind and body are intrinsically linked, and any work you do in either arena will positively affect the other. For example, by working on calming your mind using effective self-care strategies, you are simultaneously relinquishing your body's energy levels and reducing any chance of fatigue. Isn't that amazing?

BUILDING PHYSICAL RESILIENCE

 "To love a person is to see all of their magic, and to remind them of it when they have forgotten."

— Anonymous

lthough the four steps we examined in the previous chapter are pretty effective in lessening the symptoms of caregiver stress syndrome and burnout, you still need more powerful tools to overcome the overall physical and physiological burden of dementia caregiving. One such powerful tool is *physical resilience*, which centers on your ability to constantly develop and maintain a calm mood in terms of mental and physical health! However, to develop solid physical resilience, you must first understand the connection between the human brain and body, and how you can promote the health and functioning of both systems in all cases. Generally, when we hear about the term *"brain-body connection,"* most of us think of it as a one-directional process in which the brain acts as the commander, and the body responds to whatever message it gets from the brain through its neurotransmitters. Although the brain indeed dictates all the body's functioning, that fact only explains one side of the relationship between the brain and body. So what is the other side?

Every message or functional signal your brain transmits does not simply appear out of the blue. Instead, they get triggered based on changes within your body. Your brain only monitors and reacts to every change and cue occurring in your body and environment (Ask the Scientists, 2021).

To help you understand better, let's create a mental image. Think about those nights when you found it so hard to sleep well after taking a large amount of caffeine to remain energized and care for your dementia loved one throughout the day. What do you think happens? It's pretty straightforward. Your large caffeine intake triggered a significant body change, disrupting your brain's sleep rhythms and impeding its ability to produce *melatonin*, the hormone that helps to induce sleepiness.

Based on this example, notice that whatever you do with your body, whether consciously or unconsciously, has a tremendous impact (positive or negative) on your brain functioning. Thus, if you fail to take care of all these basic needs that your body demands, it might be impossible for you to have a calm and properly functioning brain. Similarly, the state and health of your brain also directly influence how healthy your body is (Wellbeing U, 2016). Hence, when you experience stress symptoms such as anxiety or the inability to regulate emotions like anger and frustration, it may be that certain foreign elements or conditions are impeding the functioning of your brain and body, intensifying those symptoms directly. So, to mark the official start of this chapter, let's examine some of those foreign elements or conditions!

ELEMENTS AND CONDITIONS THAT CAN DIRECTLY EXACERBATE YOUR ANXIETY OR UNCONTROLLABLE MOOD SWINGS

Have you ever heard of the term *inflammation*? It is simply a process that your body goes through to fight against harm from infections or injuries and heal itself afterward. So, if you get a cut on your knee, your body immediately begins the inflammation process by releasing chemicals that trigger your immune system to respond quickly to your cut. And within a few days, you see the wound healing. However, inflammation response is only sometimes this simple and quick. Sometimes it could be very chronic in that the response lasts too long with adverse effects on the body. It could also lead to brain inflammation characterized by symptoms like mental fatigue, brain fog, inability to think and process thoughts clearly and quickly, and poor mental concentration.

With time, these symptoms worsen and cause the person with brain inflammation to develop anxiety and gradually lose control over their emotions and mood. Because such a person is constantly overwhelmed with so much fear, worry, and tension, the proper functioning of their brain gets impeded to where several of its significant parts get deprived of their vital nutrients, oxygen, and good blood circulation. It sounds like every dementia caregiver's nightmare, right?

To ensure you never encounter these effects, let's examine the fundamental factors that could cause body and brain inflammation, hinder the brain's proper functioning, and increase anxiety development.

- **Dehydration**

Although the human brain and body are undoubtedly robust systems, they depend heavily on water to function appropriately. The brain derives energy from water explicitly to complete several clear thinking and memory processes and even to produce crucial hormones and neurotransmitters (Fayaz, 2022). However, it cannot store water. Studies have shown that humans lose water in every little activity or movement. For this reason, there is a strong need for us to always drink sufficient water to make up for the lost quantity.

When you fail to give the body and brain the correct water amounts they need daily, they malfunction quickly. Thus, you could get that fuzzy feeling in your head. Because of this, it becomes hard to concentrate or process other people's words. At that point, you are already going through brain fog, and if your hydration level remains critically low, anxiety sets in, and you cannot help but panic while feeling extremely weak.

- **Gut Problems**

Although there are several types of gut problems, irritable bowel syndrome (IBS) is one of the most complicated gut problems identified as potentially harmful to human brain functioning because it disrupts the critical communication transmitters between your gut and brain.

According to recent research studies, most people who experience IBS also complain of foggy thinking, memory problems, and mental sluggishness (Garone, 2023). When those symptoms continue for an extended period, they create anxiety and uncontrollable mood swings. For example, a person with severe IBS is always nervous about eating in public or at social events for fear that the food may upset their stomach. Instead of enjoying themselves when they go out with their friends, they will be worried or tense because they don't know when their stomach might upset them again.

- **Allergies**

Sneezing and itchy eyes or nose are not the only side-effects caused by allergies. As a person with specific allergies, there are other hidden side effects you might be dealing with unconsciously, including brain inflammation. Medical experts have specifically pointed out that inflammation resulting from allergies affects a person's mental functioning, brainpower, and sleep quality (Aspire Allergy & Sinus, 2019). So, what happens when you find it challenging and tiring to concentrate, sleep, or complete tasks that require mental reasoning? You are bound to get worried, tense, and anxious, and these emotions could make you easily irritated and angry at yourself and others who cannot understand your pain.

- **Illnesses and Pain**

Severe anxiety may be a consequence of several long-term illnesses, such as diabetes, high blood pressure, cancer, and other respiratory diseases because of the inflammation they cause in the brain (Schmoe, 2021). Joint and muscle pains also fall into this category. Nonetheless, the development of brain inflammation stems from the fact that this highlighted condition comes with a lot of pain which overstimulates the body and brain's immune system. Because of this overstimulation, the communication between the brain neurotransmitters becomes much slower, thus leading to slower mental speed, lower brainpower and energy, difficulty in concentration, lower productivity, anxiety, mood swings, and depression. Apart from the pain that comes with this illness, the medications administered for treating these conditions could contribute to the development of brain inflammation and anxiety (Holland, 2023).

- **Lack of Exercise (Circulation)**

For most of us, exercising is mainly reserved for people looking to lose weight or build muscle strength. However, those functions are only a quarter of the countless benefits of regular exercise. According to medical experts and scientists, regular exercise promotes blood circulation through the different parts of the brain. Did you know that your blood serves as the transport medium through which vital nutrients and oxygen get delivered to the brain and organs? When the brain receives the right amount of nutrients and oxygen it needs, bound to function well, thus creating less risk of mood disorders and anxiety (Tigard, 2022). But what happens when you shun exercising and turn a blind eye to its benefits? The blood circulation process within the brain automatically gets downturned, thus leading to a cognitive decline in the brain's power and functioning.

Lack of regular exercise also hinders your brain from triggering the release of adequate *dopamine*, the hormone responsible for helping you feel good and happy. When this essential chemical becomes deficient in your brain and body, you can do little to nothing to prevent yourself from feeling anxious and depressed.

- **Lack of Sleep**

While your brain never goes off even when you are asleep, sleep remains a very crucial recuperation period for specific neurons in your brain. Thus, when you cannot get at least five to six hours of quality sleep, those brain neurons quickly get over-worked and incapable of performing their functions properly. So, the more sleepless nights or nights of interrupted sleep you experience, the harder it is for you to think straight and remain focused enough to solve your daily problems. If, in the long run, there is still no improvement in your sleeping patterns, the different symptoms of anxiety and mood disorder automatically develop.

- **Unhealthy Diet - Sugars, Chemical Additives**

Like your car, your body also requires a constant supply of premium and high-quality fuel to function correctly. And you can only generate this fuel from the meals you eat. The quality of the foods you consume daily directly affects your brain func-tioning and mood. So, eating processed foods such as canned soups, cheese, frozen meals like pizza, salty snacks, soda, and sweets, which are high in refined sugars and chemical additives, harms your body and brain greatly. Moreover, as you continu-ously eat those processed food while neglecting diets high in essential nutrients like proteins, vitamins, and minerals, your brain function also keeps getting impaired thus worsening or triggering the symptoms of mood disorders such as anxiety and depression (Selhub, 2022).

- **Stimulants and Depressants - Alcohol, Caffeine**

In the last chapter, we established that if any primary caregiver turns to alcohol and other stimulants as a coping mechanism for negative emotions, the best option is to hand over your care-giving role to a more capable person. You become less capable of adequately delivering your roles as a dementia caregiver by consuming any of these substances as they inflame your body and brain so much that you struggle with mental focus and alertness.

Caffeine-laden coffee and energy drinks can help you remain alert through the day and night. However, when you take too much coffee daily, its caffeine content will hinder the proper functioning of your brain. It could also worsen or trigger your anxiety.

LIFESTYLE STRATEGIES TO SUPPORT YOUR BRAIN HEALTH AND FUNCTIONING

Our next task is to examine the effective strategies to improve your brain's calmness, health, and overall functioning.

1. **Stick to healthy diets and brain-friendly goods**.

Nutritionists have recommended that if you genuinely want to increase the human brain's sharpness, calmness, and physical resilience, you must consistently follow healthy dietary patterns like the MIND (Mediterranean-DASH Intervention for Neurodegenerative Delay) diet (Pearson and Burford, 2022). This type of diet stems from a combination of two effectively healthy diets. So, what use is this diet to you? First, it helps you prevent brain function decline even as you grow older. Interestingly, the MIND diet also effectively lowers your risk of developing a chronic illness like diabetes, blood pressure, and heart disease (Pearson and Burford, 2022).

Here are several guidelines for eating brain-friendly foods that you must follow regarding the MIND diet. It encourages you to stick to eating only brain-friendly foods such as leafy green vegetables (like kale, broccoli, and spinach), berries, nuts, olive oil, whole grains (like brown rice, wheat pasta, wheat bread, or oatmeal), fatty fish (like tuna, sardines, salmon, or mackerel), chicken or turkey, beans, soybeans, and so on. The MIND diet also dictates that you abstain from brain-harmful substances like refined sugars, primarily found in processed foods. In addition, you are only allowed to take nothing more than one glass of red or white wine. Any other form of alcohol could be harmful to your brain organs.

In case you decide to shop for brain-friendly foods, here are some recommended supplements that can help you:

- Omega 3s

- Zinc

- Iron

- Magnesium

- Melatonin

- Vitamin C

- Probiotics

- Valerian

- L-theanine

2. **Improve your sleep quality**.

Do you remember the night or bedtime routine mentioned in the last chapter as an excellent self-care tip? Creating a proper sleep routine to ensure better sleep quality is not only a great self-care strategy for you. It is also very effective in helping you improve your brain and body's health and physical resilience. However, someone might ask, "What steps must I take to create a sleep routine that can offer all these highlighted benefits?" The first part of a proper sleep routine centers on getting your body and brain in a state that can help induce sleepiness more easily. To do so, you must abstain from eating heavy meals or drinking anything containing caffeine or alcohol in the last hours before bed. In addition, stay away from your digital devices at least 30 minutes before bedtime to not confuse your brain neurons into thinking it is still daytime, thus delaying melatonin production. This hormone helps you fall asleep fast.

The second critical part of a proper sleep routine is making your sleeping area as comfortable as possible. This step involves regulating the temperature in your bedroom and blocking out bright lights or excess sounds that could negatively affect your sleep quality. Consider using blackout curtains if you struggle to keep your bedroom in dim light or darkness at night.

3. **Maintain good gut health**.

The most effective way to maintain a healthy gut is to keep eating food that can promote the health of the bacteria or microbiome in your stomach. When these gut bacteria are in healthy conditions, they can easily facilitate brain-gut communication, which is central to the proper functioning of the brain. Here are three major types of foods that can help you maintain a healthy gut:

- High-fiber foods like fruit and vegetables, whole grains, and beans.

- Fermented foods such as yogurt, kimchi, and kombucha.

- Prebiotic foods, including vegetables and fruits. These foods specifically help promote the growth of good bacteria in your gut, which are beneficial.

4. **Stay hydrated**.

From what we have discussed in the previous section, you already know that even the mildest form of dehydration has the potential to impair brain functioning in many ways. Thus, the only way to prevent such impairment is to stay hydrated and ensure that there is always a full reserve of water for your brain to function effectively. So how do you stay hydrated?

- Ensure you drink at least one glass of water before you begin your workout. During your exercise, you should also have a water bottle to sip water between your workout breaks.

- Drink enough water before and after every meal.

- Trade your alcohol and soda for clean water.

- Eat more fruits and vegetables with immense water content, like watermelon and cucumbers.

- Even when you are indoors and under proper air-conditioning, remember to drink adequate water.

5. **Exercise to support circulation and blood supply to the brain.**

While discussing the connection between lack of exercise and brain inflammation, we emphasized that regular exercise ensures the smooth circulation of blood-carrying nutrients and oxygen to different brain parts. But what specific forms of activities should you perform that help with proper blood circulation to and within your brain?

Interestingly, you do not have to engage in vigorous exercises like jumping jacks or weightlifting to enjoy these benefits. Instead, physical activities like yoga, bike riding, dancing, going for a long walk, or even cleaning out your garage are practical exercises for improving smooth blood circulation to your brain.

6. Getting outdoors is good for the brain.

We live in an age where we have different sources of enjoyment, like air-conditioning, flat-screen TVs, or Wi-Fi, within the comfort of our homes. As such, we often see no reason to go outdoors. However, the more we stay indoors, closed away from the gifts of Mother Nature, the more our mental fatigue intensifies. To improve the health and functioning of your brain, you need to spend more time outdoors! There are several things you can do to enjoy such outdoor moments. Some include walking with your loved one, gardening, organizing a picnic, hiking, camping, or simply sitting in your backyard. If you feel uninspired working out inside, you could do it outdoors too.

As you keep exposing yourself to nature through these activities, you will notice a gradual but effective decrease in your mental fatigue, thus making it easier for you to focus and be more productive. It also helps relieve your physical stress and unwanted or negative emotions like anxiety, fear, or worries. In short, Mother Nature can help transform you into a calmer and happier dementia caregiver.

ENABLING BETTER MOOD MANAGEMENT AND CALMNESS IN YOUR BODY AND MIND

So far, we have only been talking about how you can build physical resilience by increasing the calmness and sharpness of your brain. However, as a dementia caregiver, you will surely experience certain moments when, no matter the physical strength that has gotten packed up in your brain, it still won't be enough to help you think your way out of a problem. Similarly, it might not be enough to help overcome the symptoms of anxiety and other mood disorders. In such cases, you need your body to connect with your brain and mind to induce calmness and a better mood. But is it even possible for your body and brain to work in such a practical way? Definitely. Through the process of *somatic healing.*

Somatic healing is a unique form of therapy involving using your mind-body connection to stimulate your vagus nerve, the largest cranial nerve stretching from your brain through your belly and down to your gut (Oats, 2021). By doing so, this type of therapy helps release stress or tension from your body and mind.

Let's explore some of the top techniques of somatic healing that are pretty instrumental in calming the physical sensations in your mind and body.

1. **Sensory-focused exercises**.

This technique involves engaging your five senses to break away from negative emotions in a particular period. Doing so will restore your physical and mental calmness and boost your ability to self-regulate your mood. Sensory-focused exercises could take different forms. For example, the *5-4-3-2-1 sensory method* involves engaging each of the five senses to list the items you can observe in your surroundings.

You begin by listing five things you can see around you. Then, mention four sounds you can hear and three things you can touch or feel at that moment. Finally, pick out two things you can smell and one unique thing you are currently tasting. For each sensory listing exercise, you should focus more on things that are not easily noticeable. So the more you dig deep to observe the hidden sounds around you, the more your focus gets distracted from your negative feelings.

Another effective form of sensory-focused exercises involves creating sensory experiences that soothe or stimulate one or more of your senses. For example, you can do a scent experiment to smell different perfumes and guess the ingredients that make up each. You could make a painting combining your favorite colors to stimulate your sight. For touch, you could get a bowl of warm and cold water and, in a switching mode, place your hands in the two bowls while trying to figure out how each of the water temperatures feels on the different parts of your hands.

2. Breathing Techniques.

This somatic healing technique centers on deeply inhaling and exhaling to distract yourself from anxious sensations, release stress from your body, and focus your mind on the present moment. There are several ways you can complete this technique. Some of them include:

- **Box Breathing**

You can do this deep breathing while sitting or lying on your back with one hand on your chest and the other stomach. You start by breathing normally for about a minute in box breathing. Then, you count from one to four as you breathe in to feel your lungs with air. Next, you hold that breath for four seconds. Finally, you slowly release it through your mouth while also counting to four. Keep repeating the steps until you feel genuinely relieved from your stress.

- **Belly Breathing**

This type of breathing is also known as *diaphragmatic breathing*, which involves correctly using your diaphragm to breathe. Here is how it works. Start by sitting or lying on a flat surface with knees bent. Then, place one hand below the rib cage and the other hand on the upper part of your chest. Next, inhale slowly through your nose such that your stomach gets pushed out, causing the hand placed in it to rise. Now, hold your breath for a few seconds with your second hand firmly on your upper chest. Finally, exhale through your mouth with your lips in a pursed-shaped form. Ensure that you are tightening your stomach muscles as you breathe out. Also, try as much as possible to keep the hand firmly on your chest throughout the exercise.

- **Breathing with Focus**

In this breathing style, you will employ affirmative words and phrases to feel more relaxed as you inhale and exhale deeply. You start by getting into a comfortable sitting position, but this time, your eyes have to be closed. Then, take a few deep breaths to get your body ready for these exercises. Once you are ready, slowly breathe in. At the same time, imagine that the air you are inhaling represents a sense of calmness and peace. Then, breathe out while imagining that you are breathing out air with the stress and tension that hides in your body. You will use words to replace your imagination for the second breathing exercise. So as you inhale, you say, "I breathe in calmness and peace." Whether you decide to say it in mind or aloud is entirely up to you. So, as you exhale, say, "I breathe out my stresses and tension."

For this breathing style, set a timer of about 10 to 15 minutes. But, it is essential to emphasize that you can always switch the affirmative words or phrases. For example, you could replace "Calmness or peace" with "serenity and ease."

- **Modified Lion Breathing**

Have you ever seen a lion breathing? If you have, you already have a sneak-peak of what we will be doing in this breathing style. Start by sitting comfortably on a soft, flat surface. Then slowly inhale through your nose so that your lungs and belly get filled up with air. Once you reach the limit in which you can no longer breathe in, slowly breathe out, but with your mouth wide open like a lion. If you do it correctly, you should produce an "HA" sound as you exhale. Repeat the steps several times until you feel very relaxed, but remember to perform every action slowly.

3. **Humming**.

Humming is an activity that most of us do unconsciously or out of habit. But we must know that such a simple practice is one of the most effective stress relievers. How does it work?

As you hum your favorite tunes, you automatically create vibrations that soothe and activate the part of your *vagus nerve* closest to your vocal cords. The activated vagus nerve then sends signals that allow your brain, body, and heart to calm down while simultaneously triggering the release of *dopamine* and *oxytocin*, known as the *feel-good hormones* because they send feelings of relaxation through the body. Isn't that amazing? Even more remarkable about this technique is that you don't need to be musically gifted to hum your way to relaxation.

4. Progressive relaxation techniques.

Experts have also designed this set of somatic healing techniques to help you reduce the stress that your mind and body suffer due to your everyday caregiving roles. The best thing about these relaxation techniques is that they are easy to learn with little to no cost and pose no risk. Besides, you can complete them anywhere, at home or at the workplace.

Examples of these progressive relaxation techniques include:

- **Progressive Muscle Technique:** This relaxation technique requires that you focus on each muscle group in your body and try to release the tension embedded in them. You slowly breathe in as you tense a particular muscle group, maybe your feet, then slowly breathe out as you release it. In short, this technique involves breathing in and out while simultaneously contracting and releasing the muscle groups in your body.

- **Music and art therapy:** For this relaxation technique, you rely on elements like music, paintings, movies, or anything of artistic essence to calm your mind and soothe your body.

- **Aromatherapy:** This age-long relaxation technique involves using essential oils derived from plant extracts for therapeutic purposes. By using essential oils to massage different body parts, you can relieve your body and mind of the symptoms associated with anxiety, depression, and other mood disorder. Examples of essential oils effectively inducing calmness include jojoba, olive, and coconut oils. Keep in mind that only a few drops of these oils are enough to complete the job.

5. Getting into water or drinking a glass of water.

Can you think back to when you took a quick dip into a fabulous swimming pool and felt euphoric after coming out? As if the water had successfully washed away all the stresses and tension from the day's work? Such reactions stem from the fact that water has a powerful psychological impact on your entire being. You feel that way because that water generator has a powerful psychological impact on your entire being. And it does not matter what the quantity of water is. Even drinking a glass of water could do the magic of calming your nerves.

According to medical experts, when water is consumed by the body, it triggers your body's *parasympathetic nervous system*. Doing so stimulates digestion and lowers blood pressure and heart rate. Once these conditions fall into place, your body automatically relaxes. In fact, studies have shown that simply being near a large mass of water could be as effective as getting into it. But what if you do not have the time to get away to a pool, lake, or ocean? Then you improvise! For example, an hour-long soak in your bathtub can allow you to tap into water's calming and meditative effects.

6. Grounding/earthing.

Grounding is a therapeutic technique that requires you to perform activities that reconnect you directly or indirectly to the earth. An exercise like walking barefoot on the grass or the sandy beach during summer is a perfect example of grounding. By allowing your bare skin to directly and naturally come in contact with the earth's surface, you get filled with the energy of the ground. And that energy overwhelms you with a calming sensation that replaces your feeling of stress and tension.

Apart from walking barefoot, you can also practice grounding by lying your entire body on the ground. In such cases, your safest option is to stick to areas with grasses or clean and soft sand, like a park or beach. You also create contact with the earth by submerging yourself in a shallow pool or swimming in the ocean. However, if you do not have the time for such outdoor activities, you can also practice grounding within the comfort of your home. Also, it would be best to have equipment like grounding mats, sheets, socks, and patches (Lockett, 2019). Lying down on a grounding mat gives you the same effects as lying on the grass at the park or on the sand at the beach.

7. Guided imagery and visualizations for calmness.

This final somatic healing technique involves intentionally visualizing positive, memorable, and peaceful images or settings to trigger a state of calmness in your mind and body. For example, you could sit on your favorite couch or a quiet spot in your backyard. Then you close your eyes and focus on your mind to think or visualize a pleasant or positive object or scenario fulfilling your lifelong dream, like visiting Paris with your loved one.

Try to imagine the details, like the soft murmurs of people as you and your loved one walk towards the Eiffel Tower, the dominant smells in the streets, and the calming sensation that flows through your body as you finally set your eyes on the tower. As you begin to relax in the scenery, keep breathing deeply. After about 15 to 20 minutes, you can slowly open your eyes, having counted up to three. As you visualize and paint such pleasant mental images in your mind, your body reacts to them, causing it to relax in happiness. In no time, you also feel your heart rate and blood pressure reducing and your mind getting overtaken by a sense of calmness and ease.

Based on what we have covered in this chapter, you will agree that our lifestyle choices shape our brains, body function, and moods we have. Thus, as you incorporate the lifestyle changes, breathing, and relaxation techniques we examined here into your daily routine, track how each practice shapes your moods. Doing so enables you to understand what works best for you rather quickly.

Ultimately, we must never forget that a significant part of building adequate physical resilience lies in our ability to become more aware of our thoughts and feelings; and learn to regulate them regardless of the stressful situations at hand.

BUILDING MENTAL AND
EMOTIONAL RESILIENCE

 "A good laugh and a long sleep are the two best cures for anything."

— Irish Proverb

*I*n the last chapter, we discussed extensively how you can build physical resilience such that your brain and body remain at their best functioning even when you get hit with the most intense challenges in your caregiving journey. In this chapter, we are examining the second crucial part of the building resilience process, which focuses on your mental and emotional well-being.

As a primary caregiver, your thinking pattern and mindset go a long way in determining the level of success you will achieve in your caregiving journey. Beyond your physical state, your thinking pattern and mentality often control how you act, feel, or react to certain situations. For example, you have a judgmental mentality about becoming a caregiver to your loved one. As much as you love them, you strongly believe that it is their fault that your freedom gets sacrificed and taken from you. Such a mentality makes it easy for you to become an irritated, angry, and frustrated caregiver. It could weaken your resilience and make you more vulnerable to adverse mental conditions like anxiety and depression.

Our focus in this chapter is to explore practical strategies for building positive thinking patterns and cognitive mentality to help you remain mentally and emotionally resilient throughout your caregiving journey.

STRATEGIES FOR BUILDING EMOTIONAL AND MENTAL RESILIENCE AS A DEMENTIA CAREGIVER

1. Release yourself from the burden of self-criticism and judgment.

In Chapter 4, we mentioned that most dementia caregivers often make the common mistake of setting unrealistic expectations about their caregiving roles. We take this step to reduce our guilt toward our dementia loved ones. But guess what? Rather than helping you evade self-blame, those unrealistic expectations intensify it and cause heavier negative emotions resulting from self-judgment and self-criticism.

No matter how much hard work you put into caring for your dementia loved one, you still cannot help but criticize yourself for not doing enough. Even when everyone tells you how great of a caregiver you are, you find it impossible to believe them. When the self-criticism worsens, and you develop emotions like frustration, anger, and pain, you begin to think: "I'm such a bad person for feeling tired and frustrated while caring for my dad/mum. I'm selfish for caring about my pains. I should not be complaining about pain. No matter how unco-operative or aggressive my loved one gets, I should not get angry or frustrated. I should endure it all and still feel happy towards them." Each statement shows that you have caged yourself in the darkest box of self-criticism. And if you genuinely want to build mental and emotional resilience that can guarantee your success as a dementia caregiver, you must release yourself from that cage. But how do you gain that freedom?

You must first understand and acknowledge that you have chosen a challenging path by becoming a caregiver. Of course, there will be good days of fairytale achievements, like your loved one returning to their usual self for short periods, with no symptoms of cognitive decline. However, the bad days will also come along, and when they do, you must cut yourself some slacks! For example, on a particular day, you feel stressed from working and still come back home to resume your caregiving roles, only for your dementia loved one to showcase aggressive behaviors and refuse any form of help from you. Because of your already stressed state, you lose control instead of calming your loved one.

Of course, you will most likely feel guilty afterward, but at that point, you must also remind yourself that you reacted in a way that every average human would. So be kind to yourself and resist the temptation to criticize yourself. Instead, it would be best to focus on controlling your emotions, even in extreme circumstances.

2. **Watch your thoughts.**

Have you ever heard of *cognitive distortion*? In case you have not, it is a term that describes how humans develop specific thinking patterns that prompt us to interpret inaccurately our realities as negative perspectives (Stanborough, 2023).

The circumstances of your loved one's diagnosis could push you to develop different forms of *cognitive distortions*. For example, you could have a 'black-and-white' thinking pattern that makes you interpret your life situations only in extremes, like believing that because of your loved one's dementia diagnosis, your life and theirs will only change for the worse. It may also be in the form of *catastrophization*, where you assume that the worse will happen for no reason, like thinking that your loved one will get hit by a car simply because you got the news that they wandered off. Finally, you might be a person with a chronic mental filter who never sees the positive side of situations but only focuses on the negatives.

It doesn't matter the specific form that you experience cognitive distortions, the fact remains that such a condition is a perfect recipe for instigating different negative emotions and feelings, ranging from fear and worry to anxiety and depression. Since your emotions take their roots in your thoughts, it is only standard that you experience negative emotions when your thoughts are always negative. Thus, to transform yourself into a mentally and emotionally resilient caregiver, you must figure out the specific negative thoughts driving your emotions. You must understand that your feelings are messengers of your inner self (Evans, 2021). When you are experiencing negative emotions like fear, anger, or worry, your feelings are trying to tell you something is wrong with your inner self. And in this case, what is wrong? It's your negative thoughts! Your emotions are telling you that you need to change them. Nonetheless, having identified the elements of your cognitive distortions, your next task is to reframe them as much as you can, and there are several effective ways you can do so. First, since we know that most negative thoughts stem from inaccurate cognitive distortions, you can reframe them by acquiring factual information for clarification. For example, you often think of your loved one dying soon due to dementia. Reading a book like this can help you clarify that misconception by educating you on the fact that many dementia patients get to live relatively long lives, even with their condition.

Another means to reframe your negative thoughts is to analyze the pros and cons of embracing your cognitive distortions. It would help if you took your time to discover and understand how your negative thoughts enable you to cope with certain things and how those thoughts deprive you of certain benefits. When you weigh the two perspectives and discover the latter has more to offer than the former, you will likely be motivated to do away with your cognitive distortions.

3. Look out for signs of negative self-talk and focus on reframing that habit.

We all have an inner voice constantly chattering in our heads as we go about our daily activities. It's called *the voice of self-talk* because, through that voice, we are the ones talking to ourselves.

Our inner voices often affect our feelings and actions heavily, whether or not we are conscious of it. When it takes a supportive and positive tone, it pushes us to feel good and motivated, thus making us take the right and beneficial steps. However, when your inner voice begins to be pessimistic, it could cause much damage, especially to your mental and emotional well-being. But how do you know you are experiencing negative self-talk as a dementia caregiver? In such cases, here are some things you will hear from the voice in your head; "Oh, I am not capable enough to be a great caregiver to my loved one. I will end up failing and disappointing everyone. I can do nothing to save my loved one from dying because of dementia."

If your inner voice keeps repeating such comments, it automatically reinforces your negative thoughts, beliefs, emotions, and feelings. Eventually, it also undermines your motivation, confidence, and self-esteem so much that you may even consider giving up your caregiving journey.

Based on these signs, if you become convinced that you are experiencing the effects of negative self-talk, then I have great news for you. It is possible to remodel your inner voice such that it reframes from being a pessimistic tool and instead becomes an optimistic and motivational tool. Therefore, a significant part of building your mental and emotional resilience lies in understanding how to reframe your negative self-talk into a positive one. So let's analyze the five most effective steps to tame and break the cycle of negative self-talk.

- **Recognize the Specific Negative Thoughts that Drive Your Negative Self-Talk and Why and When They Tend to Occur.**

Before anything, you must become conscious of those unwanted thoughts that your inner voice keeps repeating. You can write them out in your journal and keep a daily log to make it easier. Ensure you remain honest and neutral, even if those thoughts are too nasty or demeaning.

It is also best to notice when these thoughts come up. Finding out the "when" enables you also to understand "why" - the exact reasons for those thoughts. For instance, the views driving your negative self-talk could be something like: "I am not capable enough to be a great caregiver to my loved one." By keeping a daily log, you might discover that the only times you tend to have this thought is when you make mistakes concerning the care of your loved one or if somebody else criticizes you for not performing your caregiving roles properly.

- **Look for Evidence to Confirm Whether Your Thought Is or Isn't True.**

Now that you have a clear picture of the thoughts driving your negative talks, the patterns in which they occur, and the reasons behind them, your next task is to research whether those negative thoughts are true or false. For example, your inner voice keeps telling you that you cannot be an excellent caregiver to your loved one because you keep making mistakes. You can inquire from other dementia caregivers or professionals to confirm if the mistakes you keep making are inevitable or if it means that you are genuinely incapable and need to improve your caregiving abilities. You can ask them to help you with tips to correct or avoid those mistakes.

- **Ask Yourself What Might Change If You Thought Something Differently.**

After confirming whether the thoughts driving your negative self-talk are true or false, you then turn interrogative with yourself by asking: "How much success would I record if I maintain my self-confidence and do my best to care for my dementia loved one? Wouldn't I be happier if I stopped dwelling on my mistakes and focused on correcting them?" Asking yourself these questions makes you consider the different possibilities of a better life for yourself, and your dementia loved one. It also ignites your problem-solving abilities. When you get overwhelmed with negativity from your inner voice, you can contain it with your curiosity rather than fear.

- **Create a Reversed, Realistic, and Helpful Thought to Replace Every Negative Self-Talk.**

Remember those list of negative self-talk statements you created in the first step? You will need them again to complete this step. All you have to do is provide an opposing positive thought that can counter each negative thinking you wrote down. First, you must ensure that those reversing views are realistic enough for your subconscious to believe. For example, if you use something like, "I am the best dementia caregiver in the entire world," to oppose a negative thought like: "I am a terrible caregiver because I keep making mistakes," your inner voice will hardly get convinced. However, a realistic statement like: "I'm learning to become a better caregiver and learning to avoid making those mistakes" could be more effective in reframing your negative self-talk.

Once you have successfully developed those realistic, opposing positive thoughts, you put them into action by saying them aloud every time your inner voice tries to whisper something negative in your head.

- **Don't Focus on Perfection, Settle for Progress.**

You might feel tempted to aim for a perfect and uncritical inner voice that makes you see yourself as a flawless caregiver. However, reframing your negative self-talk is not about transforming your negative thoughts into perfectly positive ones. Perfection is unrealistic. So, if you genuinely want to reframe your negative self-talk, focus on *who you are becoming* and *your gradual progress*. And make it the number one thought that your inner voice always repeats!

4. **Identifying the elements and situations that trigger your bad or intense feelings and behaviors.**

Apart from your negative thoughts and self-talk, several factors can trigger you to exhibit intense feelings and destructive behaviors. However, these triggers vary from one dementia caregiver to another. Nonetheless, the most common triggers that we tend to experience as dementia caregivers can fall into two categories: internal and external triggers. As the name implies, your internal triggers emanate from within yourself. They could be your emotions, physical sensations, or memories of traumatic events you have experienced before. For example, if you have previously experienced a situation where your dementia loved one got missing for days because they wandered off, there is a high possibility for such a memory to become your anxiety trigger. So whenever you are far away from your dementia loved one, you cannot help but feel anxious or worried. In fact, it might make you more reluctant to allow your loved one to leave your home. Apart from traumatic memories, emotions such as anger, sadness, loneliness, or frustration can quickly push you to develop destructive behaviors that you might regret.

External triggers, on the other hand, usually come from your environment. They could be in the form of a specific person, object, place, or situation. For example, you may get triggered by seeing the doctor who diagnosed your loved one with dementia or visiting a place where you and your loved one used to go before they got diagnosed with dementia. Or it could be when you hear sounds like somebody screaming at night, watch the news about the rate of people dying from dementia in the

U.S., or experience a breakup because you have no time for the other person.

You will notice that these highlighted situations quickly remind you of the gravity of your loved one's predicament and the harsh reality that you may soon lose your loved one. And such reminders could easily trigger you to lose control of your emotions. Hence, you must identify your internal and external triggers to build solid mental and emotional resilience. Take your time to observe as much as possible.

In the case of negative self-talk, you can also take advantage of journaling. Every time you experience a terrible feeling or react in a negative way that isn't like you, ensure that after the whole situation has died down, you sit back to recall how it all happened and what started or triggered your feelings or actions. What signs did you exhibit when you were getting triggered? Is it internal or external? Using such questions to identify the triggers makes it easier to figure out the most effective coping strategies to manage them. Fortunately, you don't need to look far because we will discuss some of these strategies next.

5. **Become less emotionally reactive and calmer.**

When triggered internally or externally, we tend to lose control over our emotions and overreact impulsively. In such moments, you cannot see the situation for what it truly is because your emotions have taken control over you. Those feelings consume you, and you feel helpless against them. Almost nobody can calm you down. To be a mentally and emotionally resilient caregiver, you must master the art of being less reactive and calm when encountering even your worst triggers. Here are a few helpful tips.

- **Charge Up Your Energy Levels.**

When you feel stressed and emotionally drained, it becomes easier for you to overreact impulsively. Thus, to avoid such situations, always ensure to develop habits that help replenish not only your physical energy but also your mental and emotional energy. Such activities include getting adequate sleep, exercising, and engaging in your favorite pursuits, such as painting, gardening, cooking, or simply hanging out with friends. On the other hand, meditation and mindfulness can help elevate your mind to its calmest state. Those activities relieve your mind of worrying thoughts and emotions to remain calm, even under challenging situations.

- **Always Take a Moment to Breathe Before Reacting**.

Even when you feel yourself getting angry and emotional, you can still make time to pause and take a few deep breaths. And as you do so, force yourself to reconsider what is happening. Ask yourself, "If I react this way, wouldn't I regret it later? Wouldn't I be hurting myself and my loved ones? How best can I handle this situation without creating any damage?" By directing these questions to yourself, you are indirectly working to take charge of your emotions. Such questions can help you develop better and more proactive solutions. Of course, it might be hard for you to practice this step on your first few attempts. However, if you set your mind to it, you can transform it into your best habit.

- **Get Professional Help.**

Sometimes, your emotional reactiveness might be too severe to handle alone. Although the strategies we examined are effective, they may not be enough to regain your calmness and freedom from your emotions whenever you get triggered.

However, with the help of a professionally trained therapist, you can get an in-depth understanding of the severe triggers driving your emotional reactiveness and how you can cope with them. Sometimes, you may need to take medications to regain your calmness. And who is in the best position to give you the right prescription? Your healthcare provider!

6. Become more mindful.

Medical experts and Psychologists have recently provided adequate evidence to showcase that mindfulness is effective for gaining mental and emotional resilience (Crumpler, 2022). It calms down your mind and serves as an effective stress reliever. But before we examine how you can become more mindful, we must first understand mindfulness's true meaning.

Mindfulness is the art of paying conscious attention to the present moment with curiosity and non-judgmental openness (Naumburg, 2022). It calls on you to take a break from your fast-paced life and notice the thoughts in your mind and the physical sensations going through your body. As you gain better awareness of your present, you feel a greater need to feel grateful, happy, and fulfilled.

The best part of mindfulness is that it does not require much time or commitment. In fact, you can practice mindfulness while doing many of the regular activities you always do in your daily life. It sounds too good to be true, right? Let's check out some ways you can practice mindfulness.

- **Slow Down.**

Today, we live in a fast-paced world where times go by quickly, and we always rush to get things done before night falls. As a dementia caregiver, the rush hour is even worse because you always try to balance two to three different lives: your personal life, work life, and the caregiver's life. As such, you hardly have time to pay attention to the present moment. However, you must learn to take things slowly to build emotional and mental resilience. Even when you have many tasks to do in a day, take a 5 to 10 minutes break and meditate in silence. Within that short period, breathe deeply through your nose and out of your mouth. At the same time, observe your present thoughts and body sensations. Ask yourself, how do I feel right now? What is going through my mind?

Take your time. If nothing comes to mind, then it's completely okay. You can observe your surrounding and enjoy the solitude until the 5 to 10 minutes have elapsed, and you proceed with your everyday life. You can also meditate to soothing music, take a short walk, or even take a long bath and sleep.

- **Simplify Your Life.**

In the previous chapters of this book, we mentioned that most dementia caregivers tend to set high expectations and goals for themselves, and such plans often create complications in their lives. Thus, to practice mindfulness and derive significant benefits from it, you must break down those goals into more achievable and realistic ones.

Creating simple plans gives you a clearer perspective of your goals. Also, it will provide you with more time to notice things you were oblivious to before. Most importantly, you can go about your daily life without feeling burdened by a long list of complicated tasks that have no essence in your life or that of your loved one.

- **Focus on What is in Front of You.**

Since you have already simplified your goals, you have no reason to overthink what will happen in the next few months or years. You must let yourself loose and focus on the things right before you. Presently, you still have your loved one with an averagely sharp memory. Focus on caring for them while also taking care of yourself. Forget about what will happen if they proceed into the mid and final stages of dementia. Forget the dark clouds that lie ahead and instead, focus on enjoying the present moment with them so that you can create great memories that can live with you forever.

- **Practice Journaling.**

Like meditation, journaling is a highly effective mindfulness practice that enables you to understand your thoughts and emotions better at a particular time. You can make it a habit of keeping a daily log of how your day went. By writing your everyday experiences, you might notice things you normally didn't pay attention to at the moment you experienced them, such as how happy you felt when your loved one complimented your cooking.

7. Embrace humor in every aspect of your life.

We all know that caring for your dementia loved one is a serious business that hardly encourages laughter or humor. However, the truth remains that if we continue to view our caregiving roles and the gravity of our loved ones' predicaments only from a severe and adverse perspective, then we are bound to get utterly consumed by the sadness of it all (Bursack, 2021). Thus, as a caregiver looking to build emotional and mental resilience, you must learn to embrace humor as you scale through the good and bad days of your caregiving journey.

Scientists and medical experts have concluded that laughter and smiles offer several health benefits to dementia caregivers and those under their care (Companions for Seniors, 2022). Apart from relieving you of chronic stress symptoms like muscle pain, increased blood pressure, and headache, laughter triggers the release of *endorphins*. This unique brain hormone causes you to feel increased happiness and relaxation. Besides, do you know the saying: "We laugh so we don't cry"? Although laughter and humor do not entirely wipe the pain you feel in your heart knowing that you are slowly losing your loved one to dementia, it makes your distress and the unique demands of caregiving more bearable.

Now that you know how much humor can contribute to helping you build emotional and mental resilience, the next question is, how do you embrace it? Here are a few helpful tips that can get you started.

- If your loved one is still in the early dementia stages, where their memory and mental awareness are still sharp, make an effort to share jokes and funny memories that compel the two of you to smile and laugh genuinely. Also, encourage them to share their funny experiences with you. Who knows? With a little push, you might find your loved one telling stories you probably never heard of before.

- You can also watch their favorite funny TV shows and movies with them. If your loved one is up for it, you can invite other close family members. The more, the merrier!

- Create inside jokes with your loved ones such that when you two find yourselves in a very tense or difficult situation, those jokes can efficiently serve as ice-breakers.

- Going through old photo albums with your loved one is also a great way to laugh.

- Away from your loved one, you should also make time to connect with fellow caregivers with whom you can share and exchange hilarious caregiving experiences other people might not find funny. Having such people around you make you laugh more and gives you a sense of belonging.

- When you make mistakes, learn to cut yourself some slacks and laugh them off.

As you try to implement each of the tips we examined into your daily routine, you must ensure that you never make your loved one or their condition the butt of any jokes. Instead, it would be best if you focused on laughing together without getting anyone hurt or disrespected.

Your thoughts are much more potent than you ever imagined. To further understand the link between your thoughts and feelings, you can do a little exercise where you track your thoughts and feelings within a particular period. The journaling practice we mentioned while discussing mindfulness is handy at this point.

Before we wrap up this chapter, here is an extra gift to make it easier for you to identify and adequately cope with your emotional triggers as a dementia caregiver.

COMMON TRIGGERS EXPERIENCED BY DEMENTIA CAREGIVERS

Make sure you have downloaded the bonus file with tips to identify and adequately cope with your emotional triggers.

Based on the details highlighted in the table you downloaded, you will see that with mental and emotional resilience, every dementia caregiver can easily cope with their triggers without allowing emotional reactivity to push them into making bad decisions. So, go for it and slowly implement the seven resilience strategies daily. But remember that this knowledge-seeking adventure continues!

In the next chapter, we will explore how you can handle the everyday challenges of caring for a person with dementia.

OVERCOMING THE EVERYDAY CHALLENGES OF DEMENTIA CAREGIVING

"Those with dementia are still people and they still have stories and they still have character and they're all individuals and they're all unique. And they just need to be interacted with on a human level."

— Carey Mulligan

So far, we've learned that dementia is a unique condition, unlike many other regular illnesses to which your loved one may be susceptible because of aging. And one of dementia's most profound uniqueness is that it negatively affects your loved one's behavioral patterns so much that these changes become unpredictable challenges that you must deal with on a daily basis.

Dealing with these everyday challenges is an inevitable and critical aspect of any caregiving. And, as a dementia caregiver, you must get fully prepared to manage the occasional behavioral symptoms that your loved one is bound to exhibit as dementia progresses through each stage. Failure to do so could put at risk both, your loved one's safety and happiness, and your own mental and emotional stability. Of course, every dementia case is unique. Thus, your loved one's behavioral symptoms may differ from other dementia patients. However, you can still take several practical steps to fully prepare mentally, physically, and emotionally for those unexpected moments when your loved one exhibits acute behavioral symptoms. And those steps are what we are exploring in this chapter. But before we begin, I must emphasize that no matter how critical your loved one's dementia symptoms might appear, there is always a way to manage them and create a strong bond with your loved one. Carey Mulligan put it more clearly when she said, *"Those with dementia are still people, and they still have stories, and they still have character, and they're all individuals, and they're all unique. And they just need to be interacted with, on a human level."*

So let's explore now the steps you can take to manage your loved one's dementia symptoms by interacting with them on a human level.

STEPS TO MANAGE THE TYPICAL BEHAVIORAL SYMPTOMS OF YOUR DEMENTIA LOVED ONE

1. Keep calm throughout the problematic episode.

In the last chapter, we mentioned that lesser emotional reactiveness and calmness are potent tools for building emotional resilience. Similarly, you need these tools to handle your loved one when they exhibit aggressive behavioral symptoms such as verbal insults or combative actions like pushing, pulling, and biting. When you find yourself in such a pressured situation, it is normal for your body to release excess stress hormones, thus triggering adverse reactiveness in your system. At that moment, your body senses your loved one's action as a form of danger and prepares to fight back the dangerous element or run away from it. Thus, whenever your loved one starts having a problematic episode, your first focus should be on calming yourself to prevent excess stress hormones and the activation of your body's negative reactiveness. But how do you maintain your composure in such a stressful situation? Remember that in Chapter 5 we examined a specific type of breathing known as *box breathing*.

This stage is the best time to practice that breathing style. Repeat this breathing exercise pattern as much as possible until you feel calm. However, there are certain situations where breathing deeply cannot effectively calm you down. In such cases, stepping away for a few seconds or minutes to regain your composure will be best. As you do so, remind yourself not to take your loved one's behavior personally because they can hardly understand or control their actions. Since you cannot temporarily escape regaining your composure, you must force yourself not to judge your loved one based on the actions they showcase. Doing so will easily make you forget the circumstances of their conditions, and without realizing it, you might get pushed to react in a way that you will probably regret later. In such a case, your best calming option is to observe your loved one and *respond only with gentle words*.

Ultimately, when you can maintain a deep sense of calmness and gentleness from the moment your loved one starts having a meltdown to the end, there is a high probability that your composure will affect your loved one positively. Medical experts have explained that people with dementia tend to mirror the affective actions of those around them (Psychological Health

Care, 2017). Thus, if you are calm, there is a high possibility that your loved one will become emotionally stable too.

2. Figure out the possible underlying causes of their behavior and focus on reducing or removing the trigger.

Having regained your composure and optimal control over your emotions, you must search for clues that can hint at the cause of your loved one's behavior. Of course, a dementia behavioral symptom only gets exhibited when something triggers it. Thus, your focus is to figure out what that trigger is. The motivation could be non-verbal in the form of hunger, tiredness, pain, fear, discomfort, or an unmet need (Ball, 2018). Or it could be physical in terms of environmental elements like lighting, temperature, smell, the number of people around them, noise, etc.

Of course, this step can be very frustrating, especially when your loved one refuses to give you any cue that can enable you to find the trigger. However, the patient is often best positioned to provide the correct answer. So, it will be best if, during that moment, you talk to your loved ones using sweet, kind, and gentle words, reassuring them that everything is alright and that they are safe with you. As you do so, listen actively to what they might be saying. Their soft murmurs could give you the cue to fish out that trigger.

If your loved one still does not provide any cues, your next option is to observe their movements, hand gestures, facial expressions, and other body movements. For example, if you see your loved one blocking their ears using their fingers, you can easily read that the trigger is noise-related. So you can check out the noise sources, whether it's the TV, laundry machine, people yelling, etc.

The most crucial step beyond figuring out the trigger of the behavioral symptom is reducing its intensity or removing it altogether.

3. Change your perspective as you focus on redirecting their behaviors.

Before any dementia caregiver can master the ability to overcome the daily challenges posed by their loved one's behavioral symptoms, they must be empathetic. Empathy within this context implies that you must put yourself *in the shoes* of your loved one. Imagine what they are going through - the physical and psychological pains associated with their condition, the fear of knowing that they are stuck with this disease for the rest of their lives, or the grief over the dreams that they would never get to achieve. When you imagine how it feels to be in such circumstances, your perspective about your loved one will change in ways you never imagined. Rather than judging them, you automatically begin to understand them. And with such understanding, it becomes easier for you to redirect their behavior and get them back to their usual self.

Interestingly, recent research studies have shown that many dementia patients, especially in the early and mid-stages, can sense when somebody genuinely cares for them (Ball, 2018). And when the realization dawn on them that you genuinely want to help them become better versions of themselves, your dementia loved one will be more willing to cooperate with you in redirecting their behavioral symptoms.

After you have successfully helped in redirecting a specific behavioral symptom, you must also ensure to schedule some time, later on, to reflect on that problematic episode. First, analyze what happened and how you, consciously or unconsciously, solved the problem. Then, concentrate on the steps that worked well in reducing or removing the trigger and what you could do better and differently if that episode gets repeated.

4. Create a calming sensory environment.

One major characteristic that all dementia patients share is that, as their condition progresses, the cognitive decline in their brains makes them more sensitive to six major stimuli: *sight, sound, smell, taste, touch,* and *movement* (Berger, 2022). Most of your loved one's behavioral dementia symptoms get triggered by overstimulation of these six elements. How do you ensure that your loved one's senses of sight, sound, smell, taste, touch, and movement don't get overstimulated? The answer is in providing a *sensory environment.*

A *sensory environment* is a uniquely relaxing or calming location designed to enable your dementia loved one to enjoy gentle and moderate stimulation of their sight and other senses. In a sensory environment, your loved one can move around freely without hurting their eyes with intensely bright light or having their ears blocked by excess noise. Usually, you find such an environment in assisted living homes and nursing homes for dementia patients. However, you can also create an exceptional sensory environment in your home without professional assistance.

Here are a few steps to transform a part or all of your home into a sensory space for your dementia loved one.

- **Keep the Room Neutral and Comfortable but Still Void of Confusing Decor.** Due to their high sensitivity, your loved one might find bright colors and complicated design patterns on the walls visually confusing or chaotic. Thus, it is always best to paint and design their room using neutral colors that they may consider visually calming. To further enhance their comfort, ensure that large furnishings such as chairs, beds, sofas, and pillows in your loved one's room have soft fabrics and smooth textures that can appeal to their touch senses. You can also include huggable soft toys or dolls, which will be placed strategically on the bed or sofa to provide an advanced level of comfort. Finally, remember that the temperature of the environment, especially that of our loved one's room, has to be moderate - not too warm or cold.

- **Install Soft "Sensory" Lighting.** Ideally, bright overhead lights are a total 'no' when you have a dementia fighter under your care. Such lights overstimulate their sights, thus triggering specific behavioral symptoms like sleep disturbances and agitation. However, when creating a calming sensory environment, the only feasible option is to install "soft sensory lighting" that is easily dimmable. Additionally, creating this environment will demand that you get blinds and thin curtains to filter out the bright rays of sunlight during the daytime.

- **Create a "Calm Corner."** A *calm corner* is a particular area in your home or your loved one's room, where you can neatly arrange the unique items that are pretty effective in helping them regain their calmness during any problematic episode. For example, some things you could place in your loved one's quiet corner include squeeze balls, ruby cubes, bean bags, their favorite books or comics, knitting yarn, etc. Nonetheless, familiarity and age-appropriateness are two significant factors to consider when deciding the items to go into that calm corner. In terms of familiarity, there should be items that quickly help your loved one elicit their best memories. Such things could be their old but unique clothes and accessories, their most cherished photos, the tools they used most in their previous job, etc. However, making the items age-appropriate centers on the need to help maintain the dignity of your loved one. These items should make them see that you are trying to respect their intelligence and capability.

- **Have a Safe Outdoor Area for Sitting and Relaxing.** A sensory environment is only complete if it brings an outdoor feel or access to the diverse gifts of Mother Nature. As such, you must ensure that within the comfort of your home, there is still an area where your loved one can benefit, similar to the actual outdoor effects. It could be creating a small but beautiful garden in your backyard or designing your balcony with fresh plants that determine constant care. You can also have a water feature like a small pool or pond in your backyard, with the surrounding area filled with smoothly shaped stones and shells. Just walking around such a backyard would undoubtedly feel like they are outdoors.

- **Stock Up on Different Aromatherapy Oils:** In Chapter 5, we discussed how aromatherapy could be a handy calming tool for you as a caregiver. The same also applies to your dementia loved one. When you have a variety of essential oils like lavender, bergamot, and chamomile, you can take advantage of their scents to stimulate your loved one into a calming mood. For example, suppose your loved one is dealing with sundowning or other sleep disturbances. You can quickly help them feel better through a therapeutic massage using any of these oils. Just remember to keep the essential oil bottles in a secure place.

If your loved one truly enjoys eating specific tasty snacks, it will be best to get them in large quantities so that you can easily reach out for them to calm your loved one down using their sensory component of taste. Who knows? Giving your loved one a pack of their favorite snack from childhood might be what they need to stop certain behaviors and instead get into a reminiscing mood.

5. Plan activities that your loved one can find exciting, fun, and stimulating.

Another practical step you can take to prepare for your loved one's behavioral dementia symptoms is to come up with an "activity care plan." To create this plan, you need to list out different activities that can serve as means of enjoyment and pleasure for your loved one, in spite of their lost cognitive abilities. However, you must avoid picking an activity that can overstimulate them. One of the best ways to ensure that you come up with the right choices is to explore a bit of your loved one's history, from their lifestyle and hobbies to their work and social interests. Knowing your loved one's past lets you easily design that care plan with the appropriate activities. Here are some extra tips or ideas to help you make the right choice.

- **Use Music Therapy.**

In Chapter 5, we mentioned that music is one of the most effective tools to improve the mood and the overall well-being of the patient. Studies have shown that music often has calming therapeutic effects on dementia patients. And, as a dementia caregiver, you can take advantage of that fact by creating several planned activities based on music. For example, if your loved one is experiencing sleep disturbances, playing songs they consider their golden oldies can be an effective cure.

You can also organize sing-along activities where you and your loved one recite the lyrics of their favorite songs. It doesn't matter if your loved one can't get the lyrics right. Keep cheering them and enjoy the process together. If your loved one is up for it, you can invite more family members to make it merrier!

- **Play Games.**

Almost everyone loves playing games, but for your dementia loved one, games could mean so much. As the patient's condition continues to decline, they may struggle with the feeling of missing out on so many exciting and fun life experiences. However, by playing games regularly with them, you get to help them overcome that feeling and replace it with a deep sense of fun. In addition, because those games often demand a lot of focus from the patient, they unconsciously develop an active mind while playing. And with that active mind, you will notice them engaging more with you and whosoever they are playing the game with.

It is important to mention that complex games are a terrible choice for dementia patients. Every game you pick has to be simple and moderately stimulating. However, you also don't want to choose a game that is too simple, thus making your loved one feel that you are undermining their intelligence.

Games such as jigsaw puzzles, card games, dominoes, snakes and ladders, or bingo are the perfect example of dementia-friendly games to help your loved one build an active mind while having great fun.

- **Lay Out a Few Repetitive Tasks.**

Repetition, whether in terms of words, questions, or gestures, is a typical challenging behavior that dementia patients tend to showcase when they get agitated and uncomfortable. However, rather than allowing the patient to engage in destructive behaviors when in discomfort, you can introduce them to practical repetitive tasks that give them a sense of normalcy and boost their self-esteem. Such duties include folding laundry, organizing simple household items by color, size, shape, or design, sorting cards, knitting, or crocheting.

Allowing and helping your loved one perform these tasks consistently makes them feel like their old "independent" selves. And even when they feel agitated and frustrated, they turn to those repetitive tasks to regain comfort. For example, instead of scratching their body or biting their nails when in discomfort, they can easily pick up clothes to fold or sort cards because it has become routine.

- **Getting Practical with those tips!**

It is one thing to read and try to gain an adequate understanding of the general tips for managing the everyday challenges posed by the patient's behavioral symptoms and another to try implementing those tips. You realize it is an entirely different ball game.

Based on the understanding that dementia behavioral symptoms can be harder to deal with, we will analyze some behavioral symptoms that your dementia loved one is likely to exhibit and how you can manage them. You should take a moment to read through the previous section again because we will refer to those points as we analyze the best management tips for each of these behavioral symptoms.

1. **Speech and communication problems.**

Over time, your loved one's dementia condition negatively affects their ability to communicate rational ideas clearly and effectively. Gradually, you may need help to understand what they are saying to you. On the other hand, this communication problem also makes your loved one more sensitive and easily irritated. Let's examine how you can handle your loved one's communication problems without hurting or angering them.

- Remain calm and patient whenever your loved one tries to express themselves. Let your loved ones speak for themselves as much as possible and avoid interrupting, even if you already know what they want to say.

- When it is your turn to speak, keep your speech short and simple to make it easier for them to understand.

- Keep your eyes entirely focused on them when they are talking or asking questions. Doing so indirectly encourages and reassures them you are interested in hearing what they say.

- Always show that you have acknowledged their speech even though it might seem out of context. And if the situation appears favorable, you can use a positive and soft tone to repeat what they have said or give more details to aid your understanding.

- Never ridicule what your loved one is saying, no matter how awkward it might sound.

- When you direct questions to them, give them enough time to respond. You can even check with them if they want you to minimize distractions such as the sound from the TV or radio.

2. **Agitation and combativeness.**

A major frustrating challenge you are bound to tackle daily is getting your loved one to cooperate with you. More times than often, your loved one will try to reject your attempts to help them. The more you try, the more agitated they become, thus causing them to resort to violent behaviors like pushing, pulling your hair, pinching, hitting, or biting you.

Sometimes, the aggressive reactions might be verbal. In this case, your loved one could harshly accuse, insult, and hurt you using cruel words. But apart from when you try to help them, your loved one could also get agitated and begin to showcase verbal and physical aggressiveness due to some external stimuli like hunger, pain, or discomfort at their surroundings.

Regardless of why and how the agitation begins, such situations may often confuse and overwhelm you. Then, how can you overcome such brutal conditions?

- Although challenging, you must remain calm, no matter how violent your loved one gets. If you lose your composure at your loved one's sudden emotional outburst, you must regain it as quickly as possible. Remember that simple breathing exercise we mentioned in the last section? Now is the best time to put them to practice while cautioning yourself not to take it personally because your loved one is not in their right mind.

- Once you are calmed, determine the cause of their agitation by following the steps discussed in this chapter's first section. However, if your offer to help turns out to be the trigger, then it might be best to step back and allow them to calm down. Reassure them that you are only trying to help and not to hurt them or undermine their capabilities.

- It will also help to distract them by playing their favorite songs. The soothing sounds from those songs could give them a better calming effect than you expected.

- You can also encourage them to seek solace in their calm corner.

3. **Restlessness and wandering.**

Because of the progressive nature of dementia, your loved one might also have unpredictable moments in which they become very restless. The desperate need to move around makes them pace back and forth continuously, even to exhaustion. In severe cases, they might wander off until they leave the safety of their homes. However, no dementia caregiver would want that to happen. Luckily, you can incorporate a few things into your daily routine to handle such situations and ensure the problem doesn't escalate. Some of them include the following:

- Stay calm and figure out why they are restless. Maybe they are in need or searching for something they cannot properly communicate. In that case, you must encourage them to tell you what they need: food, visiting the restroom, going outdoors, or needing their belongings.

- Lack of physical activity could also trigger your loved one's restlessness. In that case, you can introduce them to simple exercises which can help them use efficiently any light energy that could fuel their restlessness. It can also help in improving their declining motor skills.

- Suppose boredom is the trigger. In that case, you can keep your loved one occupied with some of the planned indoor and outdoor activities we examined in this chapter and Chapter 6. With these activities, you can give your loved one a sense of purpose and an actively engaging mind.

- Suppose the restlessness continues to worsen for an extended period. In that case, it will be best to fix an appointment with your healthcare provider, who may prescribe medications to help reduce the symptoms.

4. **Repetitive behaviors and questions.**

We mentioned earlier that when the patient is in a state of discomfort, whether physically or mentally, they do or say things repeatedly to derive comfort. You might notice your loved one continuously rummaging in drawers and closets, rechecking their wallet or purse, fidgeting, rocking their body, flapping their hands, asking the same questions over and over, etc. Unfortunately, some of these repetitive behaviors could get dangerous, like when the patients repeatedly hit their heads against walls, scratch their bodies, or hit themselves. However, before things get to such worse stages, here are some things you can do to manage your loved one's repetitive behaviors. As annoying as these behaviors seem, you should remain patient with your loved one. No matter how often your loved one repeats the same question, always try to give them an appropriate and satisfying answer.

Although you cannot stop your loved one from using repetition as a coping mechanism, you can redirect those behaviors they repeat when they are agitated or stressed. For example, if you help your loved one grow accustomed to performing repetitive tasks like folding laundry or knitting consistently, it could become their repetitive coping behavior. So, when they get agitated, wouldn't it be better if they find comfort in folding laundry repeatedly rather than hitting their head against the wall?

5. Inappropriate sexual behavior.

As the patient's condition progresses, the increasing cognitive decline they experience causes them to lose their self-consciousness and personal inhibitions. As a result, they can no longer differentiate between what's socially acceptable and what's not. For this reason, it is easy for them to exhibit sexually inappropriate behaviors in public without feeling shameful or remorse. You may see your loved one making nasty sexual comments about random people's appearance, flirting openly with them, taking off their entire outfits in public, etc.

When you encounter such a situation, you will feel annoyed and embarrassed. However, you must learn to get over those emotions quickly to correct your loved one without hurting or getting them agitated. To do so, you need to use a positive and gentle tone. Try to find out from your loved one the reason behind their actions. Maybe they took off their clothes because they felt uncomfortable.

Once you understand the reason, you can convince them to stop acting that way by gently making them understand why it is wrong. Or you can take a safer option by redirecting their attention to another activity that can distract them from engaging in inappropriate sexual actions. For instance, at the sight of their favorite game, your loved one will swiftly shift their attention and deviate from wrong sexual acts.

6. Demands and complaints.

Dementia forces your loved one to lose empathy and *emotional intelligence*. Thus, no matter how much hard work you might put into caring for the patient, they would probably never appreciate it. Instead, they might complain about many things and make challenging demands. However, whenever the patient makes an inconsiderable complaint or demand, you must again remind yourself that the person in question lacks empathy, not by choice, but because of their medical condition. That self-reminder will make it easier for you to control the annoyance and look deeper into the demand or complaints.

Ask yourself, is the complaint or demand valid? Can I do something to make their demands possible? If the answer is yes, you can adopt a positive and friendly tone to reassure your loved one that you will adequately cater to their needs. However, if the reverse is the case, you must still make your loved one feel important, believing that you will attend to their needs.

7. **Sundowning.**

Ideally, your evenings and nights are supposed to be the resting periods when you take a break from your caregiving duties and focus on self-care. But unfortunately, it will be impossible for you to have such well-deserved rest if your loved one struggles with *sundowning*.

What is *sundowning*?

It is a form of sleep disturbance condition that gets your dementia loved one in a restless, agitated, irritated, and confused mood as the sun begins to set. Unfortunately, your loved one often continues in that mood into the night, thus making it difficult for them to fall asleep and have a good night's rest. Here are a few tips to help you effectively handle a sundowning crisis.

Right from the late afternoon, you start looking for sundowning signs that your loved one might exhibit. You might notice your loved one yelling uncontrollably, being anxious and confused, or pacing restlessly. Once you confirm these signs, begin to put the proper environmental measures in place, like moderating the room temperature, adjusting the brightness, reducing the noise or the people around your loved one, and removing the unnecessary clutter around the room. In short, you remove anything that has the potential to become their trigger.

As the sun sets, focus on distracting your loved one from their negative emotions or the darkness of the night. To do so, you can offer them their favorite snacks. Or suggest doing one of their favorite activities, which may involve watching a movie, playing games, or doing one of those repetitive tasks you have performed consistently over time.

Music therapy, especially early in the evening, could also effectively calm your loved one's sundowning symptoms. Ensure you refrain from serving your loved one coffee, or any other drink containing caffeine, incredibly late in the afternoon or evening. Seek medical advice if the symptoms persist with no signs of reduced intensity.

Ultimately, every step or tip that we have examined in this chapter is crucial to your goal of offering the best care to your dementia loved one, even in the most challenging or unfavorable circumstances. However, beyond these practical strategies, there remains one critical element that you, as a dementia caregiver, must possess to navigate the everyday challenges of dementia easily. Can you guess? It's the extra support from other family members, friends, neighbors, organizations, and even strangers.

In the next chapter, we will examine how seeking and getting help from these sets of people can positively impact your dementia caregiving journey and the well-being of your loved one.

SEEKING AND GETTING THE NECESSARY HELP

"No one who achieves success does so without acknowledging the help of others. The wise and confident acknowledge this help with gratitude."

— Alfred North Whitehead

$\mathcal{A}$s primary caregivers, seeking help from others concerning caring for our dementia loved ones is often a touchy subject. Because we are so overwhelmed by guilt and self-blame, we end up considering seeking help as negligent or rejecting our loved one. Yet, we often protect our dementia loved ones so much that we strongly believe we have all it takes to genuinely support and care for them physically, mentally, emotionally, and financially. However, no matter how protective or indebted you feel towards your dementia loved one and how hardworking and committed you are in caring for them, the harsh reality remains that you need external support to survive and succeed on this caregiving journey. This does not mean that you lack an excellent caregiver's physical, emotional, and mental capability to do the job. Not at all! Instead, it only shows that you are human.

After examining everything we have spoken about from the opening of the book to this point, it is clear that looking after a dementia patient demands too much of one person. Thus, trying to complete all of these tasks by yourself will not only strain you internally and externally, but it could even make you incapable of being the best primary caregiver to your loved one. Of course, we do not want such a tragedy to be our fate. Hence, in this chapter, we'll do an in-depth analysis of the specific forms of help that are required the most as a primary dementia caregiver, the best time to seek such forms of support, and how or whom you can ask for help and successfully get affirmative responses.

Do you know that studies have proven that the best and most successful caregivers have a robust support system behind them? Yes! And guess what? You are about to become one of such caregivers because, in this chapter, we'll also examine the steps necessary to build *your support squad*.

What Support Do You Need the Most as a Primary Dementia Caregiver?

An average dementia caregiver often finds the issue of support very confusing. However, this confusion is not because we are unaware of the challenging situations we encounter in the delivery of our daily caregiving roles but because we are not sure if those situations are tough enough for us to call for help and not get judged as "irresponsible" or "selfish." But guess what? It does not matter! As a caregiver, you must acknowledge that it is always right to ask for help, regardless of how mildly tricky a problem might seem to you.

The kind of support you require the most can be divided into three categories: *physical, emotional,* and *financial support.* Let's find out what each of these support types involves.

- **Physical Support**

According to the National Alliance for Caregiving, an average family caregiver spends over 20 hours a day caring for a loved one. These statistics imply that you spend about 85% of your daily life moving from one caregiving task to another, with little to no rest or help. Of course, by dedicating that much time and energy, you will get stressed and burned out quickly. However, having physical support ensures that such an outcome never occurs.

Physical support involves getting others to take over some of your daily caregiving roles and deliver them effectively. It could take different forms. For example, you could have supportive family members, friends, or an in-house professional who permanently takes up specific roles like driving your loved one to their medical appointments, taking them out for short walks, getting medical or food supplies, cooking, etc. Or it could be that these people come over on specific days to temporarily relieve you of all your caregiving roles, thus allowing you to take a break for some hours, a day, or more.

Having those trusted fellows take away some of your roles for a few hours, a day, or days, will allow you to get an occasional well-deserved break regardless of the type of physical support received. With these breaks, you get to recharge and recuperate through self-care. It also gives you adequate time to take care of other personal needs in different aspects of your life. Most importantly, good physical support saves your brain and body system from adverse stress effects like constant headaches and body pains, sleep disorders, interference with your menstrual cycle, and risks of chronic health conditions such as diabetes, high blood pressure, respiratory problems, etc.

Being constantly overwhelmed by these adverse effects could diminish your capability of being a great caregiver. However, suppose you are always getting consistent physical support from those who have a genuine concern for the well-being of your loved one and whom you trust, your brain and body will always function at their best, and these adverse effects will be nonexistent!

- **Emotional Support**

Emotional support, within the context of dementia caregiving, involves having people who genuinely love, respect, and care about you and to whom you can freely pour out your emotions and feelings without the fear of shame or judgment. You do not need them to give you advice but to recognize and appreciate your selfless work and to listen respectfully and without judgment as you vent out what you genuinely feel about your caregiving roles, the sacrifices you had to make, and the changes you had to incorporate in different aspects of your life.

Within a day, an average caregiver gets overwhelmed with many negative emotions, from guilt and self-hatred to anger and frustration. Having people to share those emotions with will save you from burying those emotions and subjecting your mind and brain to the tortures of solitary confinement or the risk of mental disorders like depression and anxiety. For example, if you join a caregiver support group where you have people like yourself offering extended hours of unpaid care services to their loved ones, you can easily share your negative experiences, emotions, and feelings with them. And they will offer you a great sense of belonging because at least one person in that group will have shared experiences with you. Such moments of comfort help a lot in relinquishing your emotional energy and putting you in a better and happier state of mind.

Apart from these caregiver support groups, the source of your emotional support could be from other family members, a close friend, or even your therapist. What matters the most is that these people genuinely care about you and are always available when you need them to listen. With adequate emotional support, you will never consider your caregiving journey isolating or lonely, even if you no longer have enough free time or a bubbling social life!

- **Financial Support**

A significant and inevitable challenge of having your loved one diagnosed with dementia is that caring for them often comes with many unplanned or unanticipated financial burdens. The more your loved one's condition progresses, the more they require medical attention, whether with medications or therapies. As such, medical care is often costly. Lots of money is also spent on transportation to these never-ending medical appointments. Let's not forget the countless expenses for meals, repairs to transform your home into a dementia-friendly sensory environment, electricity, etc. Unfortunately, the situation even gets more problematic when we consider that your job as a caregiver might require you to take a lot of time off from work or to quit your job altogether. So, how are you meant to settle all these bills and offer the best care when you don't have a sufficient source of income? The answer is financial support!

You need other people, including family members, friends, acquaintances, and dementia support organizations, to contribute slightly or massively to your average income. And when that support money keeps coming in to supplement what you have, it becomes much easier to settle the bills, thus reducing your worries and enabling you to focus more on giving your loved one the best form of care that you can offer. But most importantly, you need adequate financial support to save you and the entire family from bankruptcy, which could automatically cut off any hope you had to improve the well-being of your dementia loved one and delay the progress of their cognitive decline.

HOW DO YOU ASK FOR HELP AND GET FAVORABLE RESPONSES?

Beyond the two primary reasons we highlighted in the introduction of this chapter, another significant factor that often holds us back from seeking help is that, as humans, we downplay other people's willingness to support us. But we quickly overestimate how much inconvenience we will cause them by asking for help. Thus, the first step to asking for help is to discard those wrong assumptions and tell yourself that every human is born with the natural inclination to help others. Scientists and Psychologists have proven this by conducting countless studies. Thus, bolster yourself with this scientifically proven fact whenever you feel like retreating from a help-seeking pursuit!

Here are four comprehensive tips to guide you whenever you need help and ensure you always get a favorable response.

- **Recognize the Specific Type of Help You Need and Make a Concise Request Based on It.**

Although we classified the support you need as a caregiver into three parts, there are many areas of dementia caregiving based on which you must require help. Thus, you might first define those areas to seek help and get a favorable response. For example, if you need financial assistance, you must figure out what specific bills you need to settle, how vital those bills are to the well-being of your dementia loved one, and how much money you need to pay those bills.

Once you have analyzed those critical details, your next task is to communicate your request to your potential helper. And one of the best ways to do so is to keep it concise and specific. Rather than including unnecessary details, focus on presenting the facts you analyzed earlier. Politely tell your potential helper the particular help you need, how much impact that support will have on you or your loved one, and how much the person will contribute, whether in terms of money, time, or energy. With such details, that person can quickly choose because they can accurately judge if they have what it takes to deliver the help you require.

For every help-seeking adventure you embark on, you must prepare to negotiate or compromise because the other party might not have or be willing to release the exact number of resources you requested. For example, instead of the $200 you mentioned in your request, they can only give you $100, accept it with a smile, and let them know you are grateful. Your gratitude can even push them to refer you to others who can equally help.

- **Avoid Apologizing When Asking for Help.**

Because you often overestimate the inconvenience our request for help might cause the other person, you may need to accompany every request with an apology. However, such apologies could reduce your chances of getting a positive response. Why? By apologizing for making a request, you not only make it seem like you are doing a bad/wrong thing, but you are also minimizing the value of the need for which you are making a request. Thus, the other party may assume their assistance will be trivial or insignificant.

Against that backdrop, you must completely abstain from apologizing when requesting help. Clauses like "I'm sorry for asking but can you...?" Or "I hate to ask but..." should not find their way into your speech. Instead, it would help to emphasize the value of your and your loved one's needs and how important the other party's help will be to your success. By doing so, you inform your potential helper of the joyous sense of fulfillment they will experience by delivering the much-needed support.

- **Make Every Request Personal and Not Transactional.**

The most effective and favored requests are usually in face-to-face encounters without reciprocity. Whenever you want to ask for help, especially if the issue is of top priority or if the potential helper is not somebody you are close to, it is best to meet them one-on-one and convince them why they are the best person with the capacity to help you.

But what does it mean for your request if there isn't an element of reciprocity? It involves resisting the temptation to support your request for help with a personal promise to repay the person by some means. For example: "If you help me, I will repay you by doing ..." This temptation often stems from our hate of being indebted to others. However, you need to realize that by offering a promised favor for the help you seek, you are making the other party feel like the two of you are making a transactional bargain and not a sincere request on behalf of somebody you love. So, what if they do not consider your corresponding promise the same value as the help they will offer you? It's simple - they will see your request as a poor bargain, thus rejecting it.

On that note, it is best to show genuine gratitude for the expected favorable response by emphasizing how much impact their help will make on improving your loved one's condition and well-being. By doing so, you have fully personalized your request with utmost sincerity, which is enough to push people to say, "Yes!"

- **Always Express Your Gratitude and Follow Up the Help with Tangible Results.**

Showing genuine appreciation is one of the best rewards you can give to some people who helped you, whether physically, emotionally, or financially. However, beyond those words of appreciation, it is also crucial that you keep the helper updated about the specific kinds of impact that their help has had on your life and that of your dementia loved one. Doing so makes the other party feel more fulfilled and accomplished. And the next time you go to them for help, they will recall the joyous sense of accomplishment they experienced. And because they crave that feeling, they will quickly give you a favorable answer.

HOW DO YOU BUILD AN EFFECTIVE CAREGIVING SUPPORT SQUAD?

- **Brainstorm and Come Up with a List of People Who Can Be Influential Members of Your Support Team.**

You and your dementia loved one are often surrounded by so many people, from your friends and those of your loved one to your neighbors and other family members. Unfortunately, not everyone around you has what it takes to be an influential member of your caregiving team. Thus, before you select people for your support squad, it is best to first brainstorm all the support options available that come to mind and what each person can bring to the table; whether in the form of time, skills, financial resources, listening abilities, etc. Most importantly, you must be non-judgmental and honest with yourself as you develop this list of prospects.

Sometimes, a particular person will come to mind because you know this person has something valuable to contribute to the welfare of your loved one. However, because of your doubts and personal judgments, you might want to ignore them. But please don't! Suppress your emotional feelings as much as possible and think in the best interests of your loved one and yourself. You might end up being surprised at how much these people genuinely care about you and your dementia loved ones and the extent of skills and resources that they will be willing to contribute to support you both.

- **Evaluate Each Person's Strengths and Assign Them Roles Based on That Evaluation.**

Once you have created a complete list of prospects that can effectively contribute and fit into your support squad, your next task is to make another list of areas where your dementia loved one requires help. Make a list of the medical care needed, transportation, feeding, finances, etc. Then, having compiled the lists, you match each prospective team member to the area where you know they would have adequate knowledge, skills, resources, and willingness to help. For every potential team member you evaluate, ask yourself, "What is this person great at doing? What specific thing do they offer in caring for my loved one? What do they have that we need the most?"

With such questions, you can determine each person's strengths. For example, your brother is a medical doctor. The medical knowledge your brother possesses is his strength. Thus, he has the best qualifications to take care of a significant part of your loved one's health care, including driving them occasionally to medical appointments, keeping track of doctor's recommendations and diagnoses, and ensuring that they take their medications and non-drug therapies when due.

We must refute the misconceptions that caregiving support is only about getting people to settle the bills. Time and an energetic personality are also some of the most valuable resources you can gain from your team members. People with such resources can save you from quitting your job and risking bankruptcy. When unavailable, you can always count on them to take your place during your loved one's lengthy medical appointments or watch over them for most of the day. Remember that every strength and resource counts, and you can always find a role that requires those strengths and resources.

- **Schedule Regular Meetings to Facilitate Consistent Communication.**

You have already reached out to all of your selected team members using the tips we analyzed in the previous section, and they are willing and ready to deliver on the specific roles assigned to them. But it is only the beginning because you are primarily responsible for ensuring that everyone performs their roles effectively. And how do you do so? With clear and consistent communication!

You must prioritize organizing regular meetings where each member of your caregiving team can talk about their progress, observations, and concerns regarding the care of your loved one. For example, the person in charge of finances can speak about which bills the team has settled and which remain unpaid.

The person who spends the most time looking after your loved one and taking care of their essential needs can inform the entire team if they notice anything unusual or negative about your loved one's behavior that might need urgent attention. Doing it this way, every member remains updated about the overall well-being of the patient and the caregiving journey in general. And, anyone can also make valuable suggestions or corrections on the necessary steps to better care for your dementia loved one. The best part of enforcing consistent communication within your caregiving team is that it makes each team member realize they are accountable to one another. And that sense of accountability reduces any chances of your loved one getting abused.

Thankfully, these regular meetings do not have to be in person. With Internet tools like Google Hangout, Facebook, and Zoom, each team member can conveniently join the discussions on crucial matters regarding your loved one's care.

- **Add Some Professionals to the Mix.**

154

The most available volunteers that you will typically contact to join your caregiving team are family members, close friends, and neighbors. But while having such people in an organized team is an outstanding achievement, there are still some crucial roles regarding the care of your loved one that these people cannot fill because they lack the formal training required to make one an expert caregiver. Hence, you must go the extra mile to find and include certain professionals in your support squad. Some professionals could include in-home caregivers, nurses, therapists, and trained volunteers based in assisted living facilities or adult centers for dementia patients. There is a high possibility that you might not truly see the need for these professionals if your loved one is still in the early stages of dementia. However, having professionals in your caregiving squad becomes compulsory when their condition progresses to the mid and final stages.

- **Identify and Make Use of Available Community Resources.**

Because of the increasing rate of dementia cases in the United States, most local communities within each state offer free resources and services for older adults with dementia care. Such free resources may center on different areas, from finances and legal issues to feeding and health care. Thus, it would help if, after creating an effective caregiving support squad, you and other team members reach out to your local community centers or government agencies to find out what free services they offer you and your aging dementia loved one.

Getting such resources and services free of charge can go a long way in lessening the financial and physical burden on you and your other caregiving team members. If, for example, your community offers free medical services in which a healthcare provider examines dementia patients, does the necessary tests and scans, and then administer free medications, such a service will undoubtedly take away a significant part of your financial burden, thus giving the whole team additional resources to focus on other important areas where your loved one requires the most help.

HOW DO I KNOW WHEN IT IS TIME TO SEEK HELP?

Gaining adequate knowledge about building an effective care-giving squad can only be relevant if you can effectively detect when you need to go out of your comfort zone and seek help. As we said in the introduction of this chapter, when you fail to get help when you and your loved one require it the most, you are automatically setting yourself up for the worst kind of burnout. Consequently, the moment you become stressed and burnout, you become an ineffective caregiver at delivering your care-giving roles and are prone to doing more harm than good to your loved one. And how would you feel knowing that you harmed your loved one? Shame, guilt, fear, self-hate, and other different negative emotions will hit you, eventually causing you to fall deep into depression. Fortunately, you can ensure that you and your loved one never suffer such a tragic outcome. All you have to do is to acknowledge the signs that indicate that it's time to temporarily hand over the care of your dementia loved one to a more capable person until you recharge and recuperate to your best.

Here are some of the most visible signs you can look out for yourself that will help you identify when is the perfect time to start seeking help.

EMOTIONAL SIGNS THAT YOU NEED HELP AND A
WELL-DESERVED BREAK.

- You feel a slight resentment for your dementia loved
  one because you now see them as the culprit who stole
  your freedom and "perfect" life. This resentment
  pushes you to avoid them as much as you can.

- You resent your loved one because you feel like you
  gave your life away for them getting nothing favorable
  in return. Instead of the fulfillment you used to handle
  whenever you flawlessly performed an essential
  caregiving service, you experience a loss of interest in
  your job as a caregiver.

- You quickly lose control over your emotions when
  interacting with your loved one. For example, you
  quickly get angry and frustrated when they do specific
  actions for which you never complained.

- You are constantly overwhelmed by a deep sense of
  sadness and hopelessness. These feelings become so
  overwhelming that you see yourself as an unworthy
  being who is better off. Such suicidal thoughts indicate
  you are very depressed and need someone to take over
  your caregiving roles.

- You wake up daily with grief and dread, wondering if
  your loved one will survive the next few months,
  weeks, or days.

PHYSICAL SIGNS THAT YOU NEED HELP AND A WELL-DESERVED BREAK.

- You find it hard to have proper quality sleep at night. This lack of adequate sleep makes you feel tired throughout the daytime, and you cannot help but take quick naps between delivering your daily caregiving roles.

- You suddenly gain an unhealthy amount of weight that can increase your risk of chronic problems like obesity or diabetes. Or it could be the other way around, where you lose an incredible amount of weight at an alarming rate for no apparent reason other than stress.

- You constantly get hit with different pains, from headaches and stomachaches to body pains and muscle stiffness.

- You also notice that the speed at which you perform your caregiving duties gets reduced drastically, affecting your ability to care for your loved one effectively.

- You keep struggling with illnesses that require urgent and intense medical attention, like high blood pressure, asthma, or diabetes.

STEPPING AWAY FROM THE PROBLEMS

While we cannot deny that dementia caregiving is a job that fills us with a sense of purpose and fulfillment, a time will come when the everyday challenges become too exhausting. Your body, mind, and soul protest at that burning point and yell, "No! We cannot do this anymore." But is it possible to wake up one day and give up some or all of your caregiver roles? Can you, who has always been a loving and selfless caregiver, take such a critical step without feeling guilty about betraying your loved one? Wouldn't other people, especially close family members and friends, judge you as harsh, selfish, and morally bankrupt?

These and other questions will occupy your mind when you realize that you need to say 'no' and step away from your caregiving journey. However, you must understand that panicking over your self-realization will only make you feel worse. Although it might seem challenging, you must calm yourself and figure out how to handle your situation. Thankfully, you don't have to look too far for solutions because we are about to examine the necessary steps to take when you feel like giving up or stepping away from your caregiving journey.

- **Establish What Your "No" Really Means.**

The "no" that your body, mind, and soul keep yelling out does not always have to be absolute. Instead, it could mean different things. Your "no" could mean, "I am tired. I need a long breathing or reflection break." Or it could tell, "I think I have gotten all wrong. Let's stop, make enough changes, and start all over." Your "no" could also be an outcry for help: "I am too inadequate to complete this journey alone. I need a massive support system."

Sadly, your "no" could be extreme, where you are ready to finally give up all your caregiving duties and dump them into someone else's hands. However, I must emphasize that the "no" of a caregiver is rarely ever an extreme one because no matter how challenging our journey might have been, we still love and care for our dementia loved one so profoundly that giving up without a fight is not an option for us. Instead of blindly assuming that your "no" means your readiness to give up every hard work, sacrifice, and effort you have made to promote the well-being of your dementia loved one, you should dig deep within yourself and find out what indeed is triggering your "no" and what it means.

- **Do What Needs to Get Done, Even If It Involves Changing Directions and Plans.**

Once you have figured out the true meaning of your "no", the next step is to focus on transforming that "no" into a "yes." And that transformation process often requires that you make massive changes. For example, such changes could include stepping away temporarily from your caregiving roles for a while, setting limits on how many responsibilities you'll be handling, getting consistent assistance from other people, or establishing healthy boundaries that enable you to adequately cater to your individual needs in the same way you care for your dementia loved one.

Knowing what your "no" involves, you must create a list of every available option to help you transform it into a "yes." Take your time as you do so. And it's okay to feel stuck, wherein you cannot think of any specific changes. However, when such happens, it is best to take a break from everything caregiving to a place of solitude where you can sometimes reflect on the successful milestones and happy moments that you have experienced throughout your caregiving journey. Then, as you remember, you can ask yourself, what went wrong? Answering that question could help you see a bigger picture of what triggered your "no" and how best to manage that trigger.

- **Passing The Torch.**

By becoming a caregiver to your dementia loved ones and constantly dealing with its mental, physical, and emotional challenges, you have undoubtedly earned yourself the title of "superhero." Thus, as much as you focus on figuring out ways to transform your "no" into a "yes", you must also accept that at some point you will have to pass the caregiving torch to a more knowledgeable and capable person, especially at the final stages of your loved one's condition. And when that time comes, you must remind yourself that you are neither being negligent nor rejecting your loved one. Instead, you are trying to protect them while giving yourself a chance to heal.

Ultimately, getting help when needed is one of the greatest gifts you can give to yourself and your dementia loved one. With adequate physical, emotional, and financial support from your support squad, you get saved from stress and burnout that a more significant percentage of caregivers today struggle to overcome. At the same time, your loved one also gets to enjoy the best care, thus significantly improving their overall well-being and slowing their cognitive decline.

In this and previous chapters, we have emphasized that caring for dementia loved ones comes with many unexpected financial burdens and legal issues. What are these financial burdens? How best can you prepare for them right from the early stages of your loved one's condition, so they do not cause emotional and psychological distress? These questions and more are what we will explore in the next chapter.

PLANNING AHEAD

"You can stress about things out of your control, or you can turn them over to God. When you release things because there is nothing you can do, you turn them over to someone who has a bigger plan and a bigger control than you."

— Amy A.

*D*id you know that the U.S. caregiver population currently spends over $190 billion yearly to cater for their dementia loved ones' out-of-pocket expenses? Yes! Even worse, more than half of these caregivers often have no choice but to dip into their lifelong savings or sell their assets to raise such a generous amount. Think about it. Isn't it scary that as a caregiver, you and your family can lose your entire life savings and assets while trying to cater to your loved one's needs? Of course, it is! But are there ways to ensure your family does not encounter such financially suffocating situations? Fortunately, the answer is yes! There are ways you can cut down those expenses so much that they hardly have any financial repercussions for your entire family. In fact, if you put your mind to it, you could get rid of them altogether. However, the key to achieving such benefits lies in your ability to gain a keen understanding of the different legalities involved in managing the likely financial situations that could arise as your loved one's dementia condition progresses. With such awareness, you and other members of your support squad can plan adequately for the economic and legal challenges that lie ahead in your caregiving journey.

This chapter will focus on creating a big picture of what this "planning ahead" process involves and its incredible impact on your life and that of your loved one. Then, we'll also explore the crucial financial and legal planning steps to ensure that you and your family never have to forego your lifelong savings or assets. Some of these steps involve detailed documentation, but fear not, because we will simplify the significance of each legal document and how you can acquire and set them up in the U. S.

UNDERSTANDING THE BASIS OF EARLY FINANCIAL AND LEGAL PLANNING

Based on what we discussed in Chapter 3 regarding the seven dementia stages, you already know that as your loved one's dementia condition progresses, they will eventually reach a stage where they entirely lose their mental capacity to make reasonable decisions about their life. Due to symptoms such as paranoia/delusion, time and place disorientation, planning and organizing difficulty, and severe memory loss, the patients lose sight of who they are. And as these symptoms develop, they gradually lose "their legal capacity." This loss implies that your loved one can no longer recognize and appreciate the consequence of their actions. As such, it becomes difficult, if not impossible, for them to execute a valid will concerning their finances and legal matters.

It becomes crucial that you, the patient, and the entire caregiving team plan ahead and set up safeguards for the critical moments when your loved one becomes legally incapacitated. And the best time to begin that planning process is as soon as your loved one gets diagnosed. At that point, your loved one is more likely to have a significant percentage of their reasoning capacity intact. Thus, the entire team can sit together to analyze and consider the potential areas of your loved one's dementia care that will require critical decision-making in the future. Medical experts and psychologists have emphasized that the two most significant areas that must get adequate consideration during this planning process are your loved one's medical care and finances.

In a few minutes, we will begin a step-by-step analysis of how you, your dementia loved one, and your caregiving squad can make future financial and legal plans to cater adequately to those two significant areas. However, before then, let's find out how much impact this step of "planning ahead" can have on your caregiving journey.

HOW ADEQUATE LEGAL AND FINANCIAL PLANNING CAN TRANSFORM YOUR CAREGIVING JOURNEY AS BEST AS POSSIBLE

The first and perhaps the best part of early planning is that it allows your dementia loved one to have a voice in every decision made concerning their life. Because they are at the center of every plan, they can easily state their wishes regarding the type of hospitals to attend, the treatment options to adopt, the people they want to be in charge of their finances, their end-of-time care plans, etc.

At the earliest stage of their condition, your loved one still knows what's best for them, so they have every right to choose. To a large extent, it also makes the journey more manageable and less burdensome for you as their primary caregiver, for you gain a keen understanding of what your loved one wants and you can focus on ensuring that most, if not all, of their wishes become realities even when they lose sight of who they are. It also increases your sense of purpose and fulfillment because, for every move you make on behalf of your loved one, you remind yourself that you are doing what they want. In cases where the decisions may seem harsh or inconsiderable, like moving your loved one into a nursing home where someone else gets to care for them or not resuscitating when their heart stops beating, you are likely to feel less guilty because you have great reassurance that you are only respecting the patient's wishes.

Planning can also become a stress-saving strategy for you and your support squad, especially regarding the decision-making pressures that will hit you later on your caregiving journey. When your loved one has already created advanced directives on how they want to get treated at every stage of their disease progression, it makes your job much more manageable. It also frees you from making those tough and heartbreaking decisions. You may already struggle with the caregiver's stress syndrome and low coping capacity at such moments. With the burden of decision-making taken off your mind, you will quickly recover from your burnout with more enthusiasm to offer the best care you can provide. Additionally, planning helps relieve your entire family of the complicated financial obligations that may likely arise as your loved one's condition progresses to the mid and final stages. How? During the planning process, you will get to know and analyze your loved one's financial capacity critically. With that knowledge, you all can suggest how those financial assets can be managed, invested, and distributed to provide adequate returns that will help settle a more significant part of their loved one's medical costs.

Although this "planning ahead" process is all about legalities, documentation, and finances, it significantly reduces the emotional and psychological effects you are likely to experience in your caregiving journey. Early planning can indeed change your caregiving journey for good by offering you lighter financial and decision-making pressure and a greater sense of fulfillment, knowing that you are respecting your loved one's wishes.

Let's now explore the steps to plan ahead to enjoy these life-changing benefits we have analyzed.

STEPS INVOLVED IN LEGAL AND FINANCIAL PLANNING

1. Evaluate the "legal capacity" of your dementia loved one.

According to medical experts and psychologists, the best time to begin planning is immediately after your loved one gets diagnosed with dementia. However, in a more realistic sense, it would be insensitive to get your loved one and the entire family at the planning table right after getting such shocking and life-changing news. So give yourselves at least a few days or weeks to come to terms with the information and emotions. Once you have that foundation set, you can then swing into action. And the ideal first step is to evaluate the level of "legal capacity" that your dementia loved one has. As we mentioned earlier, their legal capacity has to do with their ability to recognize the consequence and impact their decisions and actions may have on their lives and family (JustGreatLawyers, 2021). With sufficient legal capacity, your loved one can make advanced logical directives regarding their health care and the management of their finances.

How do you evaluate their legal capacity? By observing and analyzing the underlying stage of their dementia diagnoses, the progression of their symptoms, and their current level of functioning (National Institute on Aging, 2020). Suppose the doctor diagnoses that your loved one's condition is still in its early stages, and you also observe that their symptoms are still mild and almost invisible. In that case, your loved one has a high legal capacity level and has every right to make advance directives on how they get treated as their condition progresses.

On the other hand, if your loved one's legal capacity is not too high, he/she will need you and other family members or members of your caregiving squad to be there to guide him/her on every decision to be made. Ultimately, this step is a reminder that getting our dementia loved one an early diagnosis is a very critical part of our responsibilities as their caregivers because, with an early diagnosis, there is a higher assurance that your loved one will still have a high legal capacity.

2. Find out what the law states for your location.

Ideally, the next step after evaluating the legal capacity of your dementia loved one is to start planning correctly by setting up the legal documents. However, it is best that you do extensive research about any relevant laws within your state regarding the legalities involved in caring for dementia loved ones before starting the process (NHS, 2022). Through your research, you will learn about the state requirements regarding a living will or preparing a Do Not Resuscitate order (DNR). Although the U.S. is a unified Country, the laws could differ from one State to another, thus intensifying the need for this research. Researching is a step that must continue throughout your entire planning process.

3. Prepare the legal documents with your loved one while they are still in the earliest stage of their condition.

The documents you need to set up together vary in terms of their functions. While some focus on overseeing your loved one's finances, and assets, and handling their long-term care needs, others center on legally appointing someone to make decisions on the patient's behalf. Let's check some of these legal documents, their specific functions, and how you can set them up within the U. S.

- **Living Will.**

The Living Will directly reflects your loved one's wishes while alive and after death. In this document, your dementia loved one writes in advance the preferred decisions concerning their future care. And these decisions often reflect their religious and spiritual beliefs, values, personality, and general life beliefs. They may state in their will that they want to remain in the comfort of their home, even in the most critical stages of their dementia condition.

But what other specific things should your loved one include in their Living Will? Your loved one must specify their preference regarding medical treatment options. They also have to consider the likely critical situations that might occur in the late stages of their condition, like when there is heart failure and if they can no longer breathe on their own (Mayo Clinic, 2022).

Will they want their medical doctors to use measures like cardiopulmonary resuscitation (CPR) or a ventilator to extend their life in such situations? Or, do they have any specific circumstances in which they would prefer the doctors to let them go? Answers to such sensitive questions must be present in the Living Will.

They must also state how they want their caregiving team and medical experts to handle any pain management and comfort care (Mayo Clinic, 2022). Would they prefer taking a lot of antibiotics and antiviral drugs to fight the increasing infections that may arise as their condition progresses? When they can no longer eat, drink, and excrete normally, do they want to rely on external supports like a feeding tube? When do they prefer to start the feeding tube nourishment, and how long do they want to rely on it for their daily energy supply? (Mayo Clinic, 2022).

Similarly, in the late stages of dementia, your loved one's kidneys are likely to fail requiring dialysis (Mayo Clinic, 2022). Hence, your loved one also has to determine within their Living Will if they want dialysis or if they want to extend their lives through the help of dialysis. Through dialysis, a machine will remove waste products and excess fluid accumulated in the body.

Your duty is to support the patient and share your opinions, concerns, and perspective on these important decisions. But you must be subtle in your guidance and not demand or enforce your opinions because every instruction included in this legal document must be of your dementia loved one's will.

A key person when writing a Living Will is the medical health-care provider. With a medical professional in the picture, your loved one can inquire about any medical decisions they may have to make as their condition progresses. The doctor is in the best position to tell which decisions are feasible and effective for the patient's overall well-being and for the mental and emotional state of their caregivers, family members, and friends.

Ultimately, a Living Will will also serve as the legal document in which your loved one declares their end-of-life decisions, like how their money and assets will get distributed to their loved ones and what they want to do with their body after their demise (Silverman, 2021). For example, your loved one could state that they want to be buried at a particular location with a funeral ceremony, surrounded by family and friends. Or, your loved one might prefer his/her body for effective health procedures like tissue and organ donations or to donate their body for scientific studies.

Writing a Living Will could be complicated based on the different aspects to be considered. To help with the process, you can hire a *solicitor* to help your loved one set up their Living Will. You can also search online for legal websites that offer you and your family member free advice and samples of Living Wills that can guide you on how to create one (Silverman, 2021). Once the Living Will is ready, the next step is to legalize the document with a notary official appointed by the state. They will stamp the document with their notary stamp to make it official and legally binding. In the end, it is best to make several copies of this Living Will to share it with your family members and with all healthcare providers involved in your loved one's care.

- **Do Not Resuscitate Order (DNRO).**

A DNRO is a simple advance directive that your dementia loved one can redact. It instructs their healthcare providers not to perform cardiopulmonary resuscitation (CPR) or use ventilators when their heart stops beating. By creating this order, your loved one is expressing his/her wishes of whether they want doctors to extend their lives by any means possible, or if they should let them go to rest in peace. Although it might be painful to know that your loved one wants to make such a sensitive declaration, you still have to help them set it up. So how can you help your dementia loved one set up a DNR Order in America?

A DNRO is relatively easy to set up. All your loved one has to do is express their preference regarding resuscitation to their medical doctor. They could deliver this order verbally or in a written format. Then, the doctor will boldly spell out the demands on paper, sign them, and give them to your loved one for signature. You might also have to sign as their witness. Once the signing is completed, the doctor places the written order in your loved one's medical record. However, whenever your loved one changes hospital locations, you will have to repeat the process of signing a new document for that other hospital. For this reason, it's best to have a notarized DNR document you can provide to each hospital or medical facility.

- **Power of Attorney (POA) and Health Care Power of Attorney (HCPOA).**

A Power of Attorney document is a legal authorization document that proves that your dementia loved one has given a particular person the right and authority to act and make decisions on their behalf (Hayes, 2022). The person who receives the power is known as the *agent* or *attorney-in-fact*.

In America, there are two types of Power of Attorney documents that patients with terminal illnesses can set up. The first POA type focuses mainly on a person's finances, while the other focuses on health care. These two POA documents are essential when planning for your loved one's dementia care.

With the *Health Care Power of Attorney* (HCPOA), also known as *Health Care Proxy* (HCP), an agent can make justified decisions on the specific treatments that your dementia loved one receives, and the facilities chosen, like hospitals or healthcare providers, and care facilities (nursing homes, assisted living facilities, or in-house caregiving) they will move to when they approach the mid stages of their dementia condition (Hayes, 2022). It also gives the agent the power to decide what end-of-life procedures your loved one takes in their most critical situation.

On the other hand, the *Financial Power of Attorney* (FPOA) gives an agent the authority to manage and control the financial affairs of your dementia loved one. Such matters include making deposits and withdrawals, signing checks, paying bills and filing taxes, and managing investment accounts, assets, etc. (JustGreatLawyers, 2022).

Although signing either POA can help guarantee that the financial and health needs of your loved one get adequately catered for, it comes with the same amount of risks. It's like signing a blank check of your life. For this reason, your dementia patient must carefully select the agent or attorney-in-fact of their choice. This person should have earned the patient's trust. They must be ready to fulfill your loved one's wishes and look out for their best interests in critical situations.

Who can become your loved one's agent or attorney-in-fact? It could be you or any other person as long as the patient trusts and believes that person will make decisions that respect their wishes and values. More importantly, this person has to fulfill your residential state's criteria for a health or financial attorney-in-fact. In some states like California, you must be over 18 years old to become an agent. So as long as you meet that requirement, you, as the primary caregiver, could also double as your loved one's attorney-in-fact.

Now that you know what a Power of Attorney involves, its types, and its relevance to the well-being of your loved one, let's find out how you and your dementia loved one can set it up in the U. S.

How Can You Set Up a Power of Attorney or POA for Your Dementia Loved One?

- **Get the Correct POA Form that Follows the Requirements of Your State.**

There are two ways you can acquire a POA form. You can get it from a lawyer, online, or purchasing one. Just remember that the POA requirements and procedures differ from state to state. While some states' POA may demand only the signature of your loved one and their agent, others may require the notarization of both your loved one's signature and a third party as a witness (Hayes, 2022).

Getting the correct forms is important because they will have the provisions required by the State. Without those provisions, it will not get accepted by any court of law in your particular State. To confirm the suitability of a POA form, your best option will be to consult a lawyer. However, you can also search online for information about what your State's POA should contain or ask for help from a local estate planning expert.

- **Identify Each Party and Delegate Powers.**

After getting the correct POA forms, the next step is to identify in writing the person granting the POA, which is your loved one, and the individual to whom they are granting the right and power to make decisions on their behalf. Upon completing the identification process, your loved one will highlight each area of power they are ready to grant to their agent. Although your loved one still has adequate mental capacity, you and other members of your caregiving teams can guide them on which powers to give out and which not to. Of course, under United States laws, there are certain powers that a citizen cannot delegate to another person. For example, the right to vote and the ability to make, alter, or cancel a Living Will. Apart from these powers, your loved one can also withhold some powers from their attorney-in-fact, like taking off life support at the critical point of their illness.

Your loved one must also specify the durability of the POA or how long is it meant to last. Usually, a POA signed for dementia care tends to be very durable, which means that it stays from the point of its signing to the principal's demise. However, your loved one could set certain conditions based on which the POA can be revoked from one person and given to another. For example, if the agent gets ill and can no longer deliver the responsibilities assigned to him/her, your loved one could select someone else as a backup plan. Just make sure this is stipulated in the POA.

- **Ensure that Every Piece of Information Is Written Down and Recorded.**

Although there are a few states in the U. S. that accept verbally granted POA to an attorney-in-fact, it is most reliable and least risky to set up a written POA, spelling out the details word-for-word, from the names of the parties involved to the specific powers granted to the agent or agents, and the underlying conditions of the contract. Having a written POA cuts out any chances of arguments or confusion, especially between family members. You can also go the extra mile and create a formal record that shows that such a document exists. Depending on the requirements in your State, this step may or may not be compulsory.

- **Get the Necessary Signatures and Notarize the Document.**

The standard signatures that a State or court of law often demands on a POA are those of the principal and the agent. However, in some States like Ohio, you must further notarize the document after getting them signed by the parties involved. The notary then certifies the authenticity of the signatures using a notary stamp. Quite simple, right? But mind you, this notarization service may not be free of charge, and it varies from state to state.

- **Filing the Document to The Court of Law.**

Once you have the POA written, signed, and notarized, your last step is filing it to a court or government agency. And if it gets accepted by the court, then the POA between your loved one and their agent or agents automatically becomes valid and legally binding for as long as the durability stands.

4. **Create a Trust with Your Dementia Loved One.**

This step solves the question of how your dementia loved one's assets can get adequately managed, invested, and distributed after their demise. Doing so will help ensure these assets generate enough funds for future care.

So, what is a Trust? It is an independent legal entity that your loved one can set up to hold their assets, with underlying stipulations on how these assets will get managed and invested while they are living and how their family and friends will distribute each property and assets after their demise (Freewill, 20221). Having set up a Trust, your loved one has to select a trustee who will be in charge of managing those assets, although under the directives of your loved one. To a large extent, a Trust is a perfect complement to your loved one's living will. It elaborates more than a living will on how your loved one wants the entire family to handle the financial aspect of their life while they are still living and after their death. As with the POA, anyone could get selected as a trustee if your loved one considers such a person capable of managing their finances and assets (Derpersio, 2022). As a primary caregiver, you could also serve as their trustee. Another family member who is a member of the caregiving squad can also take up this role. Sometimes, the entire family prefers to hire a financial professional as their trustee.

Within the U. S., there are two types of Trusts: *Revocable* and *Irrevocable* Trust. A *Revocable Trust* is the type of Trust that your loved one can set up when they are still alive, enabling them to modify specific terms or conditions of the agreement at any time. For example, they could replace the appointed trustee and the conditions or stipulations they designed concerning their assets' management, investment, and distribution after their demise (Derpersio, 2022). Your loved one may also select you to become a *Supportive Trust Protector*. That position allows you to oversee the affairs of the trustee and automatically get equal rights with your loved one to revoke the terms and conditions of their revocable Trust.

On the other hand, an *Irrevocable Trust* is a legal entity set in stone from the very moment your loved one appends their signature on it. Except under the rarest circumstances, which often involve a court order, nobody, not even your loved one who created it, can make any alterations to the Irrevocable Trust (Derpersio, 2022). In spite of its risk tendency, an Irrevocable Trust can be advantageous, for it does not come with tax charges, thus increasing the income generated from a person's assets. Nevertheless, because of the rigidity and risky nature of the Irrevocable Trust, legal experts have emphasized that a Revocable Trust is most suitable for planning and providing for a loved one's future dementia care and creating a smooth pathway through their successors or beneficiaries ensuring their wishes become realities. Also, with a *Revocable Living Trust*, after your loved one's demise, their assets will get easily distributed or transferred as directed in terms of the Trust, thus cutting out any prolonged stress, disruption, or costs that could result from a *Probate* or other court processes.

Setting up a Trust in U. S. today can be pretty complicated. Thus, it is best to reach out to a lawyer in your residential State who can guide you and your dementia loved one through the process. However, if you believe that the Trust your loved one intends to set up is relatively straightforward, you can search online for websites that help clients create their own *Revocable Living Trust* for a set charge. One such website is www.freewill.com.

5. Get legal guardianship or conservatorship from the court.

Some may wonder what happens if we discover that our loved one has lost a more significant part of their legal capacity at the time of evaluation. In that case, it will be too difficult for them to take steps such as writing a living will, setting up a Trust with terms and conditions that a trustee has to offer, or selecting an attorney-in-fact and granting them a POA. Such steps require serious decision-making that a dementia patient with low cognitive capacity cannot complete. So, how do you and your caregiving team plan for your loved one's future care in such circumstances? Through *Guardianship*!

Guardianship, sometimes called *Conservatorship*, is a legal procedure in which a court appoints a "Guardian" to make decisions and manage the health and financial-related affairs of persons with cognitive-declining illnesses like dementia (Raphan, 2022). Since your loved one has neither legally authorized anybody to act as their agent nor made any future care plans for when they become mentally incapacitated, you, as the primary caregiver or any other family member, have the legal right to request through a series of court proceedings to become their guardian. However, each State in the U. S. has specific laws and requirements concerning a guardianship proceeding, hence the need for adequate research.

To acquire guardianship of your dementia loved one, you begin by getting the court's guardianship request forms and papers. Then you fill them out with the necessary details and file them back to court for a date. As you take this step, you must notify other family members of the request you sent to the court. You could also give them each a copy of the court papers. Having received your request, the court will appoint an Investigator (also known as a *Court Evaluator*) to examine the circumstances surrounding your request and your loved one's condition. And in doing his job, the Court Evaluator will conduct several interviews with you, your loved one, other family members, and the healthcare provider in charge of your loved one (Raphan, 2022).

They may also review necessary materials like your loved one's medical records and financial documents.

Eventually, the Court Evaluator concludes the investigation and then issues a written report with recommendations to guide the judge in their decision-making. After submitting the information, the court will send a date for the guardianship proceedings. Finally, the judge will determine if your loved one is mentally incapable and needs a guardian for their safety and well-being. Ultimately, if the judgment turns out to be favorable, you will get appointed as your loved one's legal guardian. However, the judge will be the one to determine the areas of your loved one's life to which you can exercise total authority, although the functions usually highlighted center mostly on their health care and finances.

Although the legal and financial planning process we examined in this chapter can be pretty long and temporarily stressful, its benefits to you and your dementia loved one exceeds its lengthiness. More importantly, you will enjoy the financial and psychological benefits of early planning as you continue to be a caregiver to your dementia loved one, even after their death. And it all begins with taking that first step of evaluating your loved one's legal capacity, and before you know it, you are at the end of the planning process!

IN THE END

 "Don't send me flowers when I'm dead. If you like me, send them while I'm alive."

— Brian Clough

a s your loved one's dementia condition approaches its end-of-life phase, most caregivers automatically experience a more intensive and burdensome form of emotional and psychological distress for several reasons. First, your loved one requires a more specialized set of comfort care that is pretty different from what you have helped administer to them from the moment they first got diagnosed. Such a form of care often involves *hospice care services.*

Studies have shown that a more significant percentage of caregivers in the U. S. today barely understand what these services entail. This lack of understanding often makes helping your loved one transition to end-of-life care more challenging and confusing. Beyond this confusion, your loved one's end-of-life care will probably leave you emotionally drained, especially if you are not mentally or emotionally prepared. Moving your dementia loved one into a nursing home often marks the onset of mourning and grief for most primary caregivers. From that moment, no matter how much we try to stay strong for our loved one and other family members, the reality that our loved one is only a few steps from leaving us behind keeps hitting us, thus making us more dreadful and pushing us deeper into the dark hole of grief and depression. But what happens if you get mentally, emotionally, and psychologically prepared for the changes bound to happen before your loved one approaches the end stages of life? Then, the journey becomes less challenging and emotionally burdensome. Although the truth remains that this preparation will not prevent you from experiencing the inevitable grief that you will encounter in the end, it will go a long way in equipping you with strategies to help you better handle these different issues that are likely to develop.

Luckily, this chapter is all about giving you that must-needed preparation. We will begin by analyzing the differences between the two most common care types available for dementia patients: *hospice* and *palliative* care. We'll also explore why and how you can honor your loved one's wishes and spiritual beliefs while providing for their end-of-life care. Preparing for your loved one's end-of-life stage also involves planning for what happens after their death. Thus, we will examine the steps to take when planning for your loved one's funeral or memorial services and the effective coping strategies to implement in your daily routine to help you better deal with their death. This chapter marks our last ride on this knowledge-seeking journey.

UNDERSTANDING THE DIFFERENCE BETWEEN
HOSPICE AND PALLIATIVE CARE

At least once during the first few months of your caregiving, you will constantly encounter the terms *palliative care* and *hospice care*. And the popularity of these terms centers on the fact that they are care services specifically designed to offer comfort and relief to people with severe illnesses and conditions like cancer, chronic heart failure, and dementia. Because of the similarities in their objectives, people tend to use these terms interchangeably. However, they are quite different in several significant ways. To show these differences, let's start by analyzing what palliative care involves.

According to medical experts, *palliative care* is a type of medical care that centers on reducing or eliminating the physical and mental symptoms showcased by patients with long-term illnesses like cancer and dementia (National Institute of Aging, 2021). It also involves helping patients and their families make important decisions about the patient's treatment while offering them emotional, financial, and spiritual support. The purpose of *palliative care* is to improve the patient's care and their family's overall quality of life. Because it is a form of comfort care with or without curative intent, we consider palliative care a suitable option for terminally ill patients. Thus, you can get your loved one to begin palliative care immediately after they get diagnosed with dementia or at the latter stages of their illness when it is impossible to cure them.

On the other hand, *hospice care* offers care, relief, comfort, and improved quality of life to patients whose terminal illnesses are at their end stage with no hope of recovery. Unlike palliative care, hospice care does not attempt to cure dementia symptoms or slow down the disease's progression. Instead, it centers on offering temporary relief from their symptoms and comprehensive comfort care within the short period they have left to live.

Let's illustrate the differences between palliative and hospice care. When your loved one becomes diagnosed with dementia, placing them under palliative care is a perfect idea; they will undergo different treatments to manage their symptoms better, slow their cognitive decline and prolong their life. However, as they progress to stages 6 and 7, which we know to be the advanced stages, the medical professionals in charge of palliative care will inform you that your loved one is now at their end-of-life phase with maybe only a few months left to live. As such, your loved one has to get transferred into hospice care, which automatically leads to the total stoppage of all the treatments your loved one has been getting to cure their symptoms or prolong their lives.

The hospice team will only focus on offering your family member 24/7 care services that involve pain management, symptom relief, and emotional support – all of which would not result in an extended life span for your loved one. Hospice care is indeed the most suitable option of care for your dementia loved one at their most critical end-of-life phase because palliative care is not effective at that point, for they have no hope of recovering, no matter how much curative treatment gets administered. So, why not focus on making your loved one's last few months as painless, peaceful, and stimulating as possible?

HOW DO YOU KNOW THAT YOUR LOVED ONE NEEDS HOSPICE SERVICES?

Studies have shown that many caregivers often need clarification regarding the perfect time to sign their loved one for hospice care services. While some usually wait too long and fail to get their loved one to begin their hospice care soon enough to benefit from its full and meaningful advantages, others jump the gun and try to sign their loved one up for hospice care when the latter is not yet to receive the full benefits of this particular care. Hence, as a primary caregiver, you cannot afford to be too early or late regarding your loved one's introduction to hospice care because timing significantly determines how much the patient and your loved one will benefit from the care. So, what signs should you look out for to recognize appropriately and timely when your loved one becomes eligible for hospice care?

The number one criterion of hospice care eligibility is for your loved one's healthcare providers to diagnose and evaluate that they have not much time than six months to live if their dementia condition keeps progressing at its natural course. Apart from this six-month prognosis from the doctor, you also notice that your loved one probably has completely lost their ability to walk, eat, or move any part of their body, thus causing them to soil themselves frequently with no means to clean up properly. They may find it impossible to speak more than a few words daily or to make facial expressions like smiling or frowning. You may also realize a drastic increase in the number of times your loved one gets hospitalized or has to visit the doctor. Although you might not have gotten an official six months prognosis from your loved one's doctor, these symptoms are still clear signals that it might be the perfect time to contact the hospice care service. Thus, you can relay your suspicions and observations to the doctor for confirmation.

Ideally, when you share your intention to sign up your loved one for hospice, the experts in the hospice care facilities will evaluate the patient using *The Dementia Fast Scale*. The team will use this testing scale to measure the time rate at which the patient responds in critical areas like mobility, and determine if the patient is eligible for hospice (Hospice Care Option, 2022). The slower their response time, the higher their qualification score on the scale. Usually, the most eligible hospice candidate has a score of seven and above, which often results from the fact that they constantly exhibited the symptoms we highlighted earlier.

PROS AND CONS OF UTILIZING HOSPICE SERVICES

Stopping our loved one's curative treatments and moving them to hospice care is undoubtedly one of the most challenging decisions you must make. Understanding the advantages that hospice care can offer your dementia loved one and the entire family helps make you less hesitant to choose correctly. More importantly, it could lessen the psychological and emotional distress you will likely experience during decision-making.

As a primary caregiver, you must know the downsides that come with getting your loved one into hospice care, for such knowledge will help you compare the pros and cons to determine if hospice care is the right choice for your dementia loved one and the entire family. So let's first identify these pros and cons to enable you to make that comparison and prepare ahead.

THE PROS

- **24/7 Comprehensive Support and Comfort from an Impressive Interdisciplinary Team.** Putting your loved one under hospice care gives them immediate access to care providers who are always available to offer round-the-clock assistance. Interestingly, the hospice care team usually comprises professionals from a wide range of important medical and non-medical disciplines, including doctors, nurses, physicians, counselors, social workers, chaplains, and home health aides. With this diversity in staff expertise, hospice care can easily cater to the medical, spiritual, mental, and emotional needs of your loved one while offering emotional and psychological support to family members, especially you, the primary caregiver.

- **Insurance Helps Reduce Your Loved One's Expenses.** Transferring your loved one to hospice care also comes with a lesser financial burden which is a significant boost for you and your entire family after spending an outstanding amount of money on your loved one's dementia care for so long. Federal health insurance programs like Medicare and Medicaid typically cover most of the charges and out-of-the-pocket expenses related to the care that a dementia patient receives. Thus, when your loved one becomes a part of the hospice care program, you will have little to worry about concerning the medical bills, thus giving you more chance to focus on other aspects of their end-of-life care.

- **It Relieves Your Loved One of Unwanted and Painful Medical Treatments.** Most medical treatments, especially the medications often administered to dementia patients, may have painful side effects like headaches, vomiting, nausea, and constipation. Unfortunately, your loved one may have to endure this pain and discomfort without the treatment, positively affecting their health. However, by switching to hospice care, your loved one would not have to deal with such painful curative treatments but bask in adequate comfort care, focusing on helping them live their best quality of life while fulfilling some, if not all, of their last wishes.

- **It Offers a Great Sense of Satisfaction to You and Your Entire Family.** While there is always a chance that you'll feel bereaved to put your loved one under hospice care, knowing that your loved one is getting the best quality of care from professionals will surely calm you down, thus making you feel satisfied. Moreover, when you think about the 24-hour daily care from experts that your loved one constantly gets, you know deep within yourself that there is no better way to give your loved one a peaceful and calming end than to free them from painful treatment, and instead, have them taken care of by those trained to deliver the best care.

Of course, these highlighted advantages will probably motivate any caregiver to believe that hospice care is the right choice for their loved one in their end-of-life phase. But just before you make that decision, you must acknowledge a significant downside of hospice care.

THE CONS

- **Your Loved One Might Get Denied Specific Diagnostic Testing.** Diagnostic testing often involves those seeking curative treatments. Thus, as a patient under hospice care, your loved one is not expected to require such testing. However, there might be a few situations where their doctor demands that they get diagnostic testing, such as X-rays and blood tests, to understand how to help your loved one manage their pains more efficiently. Unfortunately, in such situations, the hospice care center may not offer such testing services as they would consider it too expensive with little to no benefits to their goals of giving comprehensive end-of-life comfort care. Thus, if your loved one's attending physicians make such tests mandatory, they may have to do it elsewhere, increasing out-of-the-pocket expenses as external services beyond hospice care services are not covered by insurance. And the more tests required, the higher the costs you will have to settle. Eventually, their medical expenses could exceed what the insurance offers.

HONORING YOUR LOVED ONE'S WISHES

Beyond signing up your loved one timely for hospice care, another significant part of their end-of-life care centers on honoring their wishes. Remember we stated in the last chapter that your loved one must identify and analyze all their end-of-life wishes in their Living Will before they lose their legal capacity? Therefore, the stage at which your loved one begins hospice care is also the perfect time to ensure that every wish highlighted in their Living Will gets respected.

An excellent place to start is to consider where they have chosen to have their hospice care and pass away, whether it's within the comfort of their home, nursing home, assisted living facility, or hospice care center. It would be best if you also considered their wishes regarding medical care. If they have already signed a DNR Order, you must ensure that no doctor tries to extend their lives after their heart stops pumping. The same applies regarding their wishes about feeding tubes, dialysis, and other dementia coping treatments. To make this task easier for yourself and your family, make copies of every advanced directive and statement your loved one made concerning their care and share them with their hospice care team to ensure they genuinely understand your loved one's wishes.

Ultimately, it is crucial for you to make an intentional effort to ensure your loved one's wishes get honored. Doing so fills you with a greater sense of fulfillment and purpose. And even when your loved one finally passes away, you would likely not be overwhelmed with guilt, for you know you did what they wanted while working hard to give them the best quality of comfort and care during their end-of-life phase.

HONORING THE SPIRITUAL BELIEFS OF YOUR DEMENTIA LOVED ONE

In the last chapter, we mentioned that the content of your loved one's Living Will directly reflects their personal values and spiritual beliefs. It is also important that you respect your loved one's spiritual beliefs. This explains why spiritual care plays a significant part in hospice care. As the primary caregiver, you can work closely with the chaplain or spiritual advisor in the hospice team to make them understand your loved one's spiritual beliefs. The spiritual advisor can then deliver adequate spiritual counseling that will have calming and uplifting effects on your loved one.

Although your loved one may have forgotten who they are and most of their life memories, the person inside is still deeply connected to their spiritual beliefs. For this reason, it is imperative to find a trained hospice spiritual advisor or priest who can offer your loved one spiritual insights and inspiration in their end-of-life phase. Such wisdom and inspiration reawaken their spirit and emotions, ease their fear and anxiety of death, and push them to let go of any life regrets they might have. In the end, honoring your loved one's spiritual beliefs and giving them adequate spiritual care leave them feeling free, joyfully fulfilled, and at peace to begin their journey to the afterlife.

PLANNING FOR YOUR LOVED ONE'S FUNERAL OR MEMORIAL SERVICE

In the same way, you conduct financial and legal planning for your dementia loved one ahead of their end-of-life phase, you also have to get them to express their wishes regarding a funeral or memorial service. Such advanced planning saves you and other surviving family members from getting stressed and confused about how best to bury your loved one while you are still battling with the grief of their death. Of course, discussing their end-of-life wishes regarding their funeral will surely be emotionally burdensome, for it is an obvious reminder that you will lose your loved one soon. However, you must stay strong by reminding yourself that it is only by getting your loved one's wishes early on that you can ensure their preferences are respected, even after their demise. Ultimately, all that matters is that you want to give your loved one the celebration of life that they genuinely want and deserve.

STEPS TO PLAN FOR YOUR LOVED ONE'S FUNERAL OR MEMORIAL SERVICE

- Start by asking how they would prefer their body to get disposed of after death. Is it through a traditional burial process or cremation? Inquire if they have any meaningful or memorable location that they wish to be their ultimate resting place.

- Equipped with that information, you can gradually push forward and then coax your loved one into describing a visual image of how they want their funeral or memorial service to hold. You might be shocked to see your loved one voluntarily sharing details of their vision, including the location of the memorial service, the set of people that they want to be there, the genre of music to play, flowers and decorations to use, etc.

- Finally, analyze the expenses such as the funeral arrangements expenses. Then, the whole family could decide if you want to opt for a pre-plan burial option, which can help reduce immediate costs.

TIPS AND RESOURCES TO HELP YOU, AS A CAREGIVER AND SURVIVOR, DEAL MORE EFFECTIVELY WITH GRIEF AFTER YOUR LOVED ONE'S DEATH

From the moment our loved one gets diagnosed with dementia, grief becomes familiar to us. We pass through different stages of grief, from guilt and denial to sadness and pain, as we watch our loved ones lose significant parts of themselves daily. And when we finally lose them to death, we undoubtedly experience grief in its most intense forms. That intensity hits us so hard that we get pushed to indulge in the worst of habits, like excessive alcohol drinking, smoking, self-harm, and any other thing that can give us a temporary escape from our reality. But you must ask yourself, would my loved one be happy or satisfied watching me in this state? Absolutely not! We cannot let our grief consume us, no matter how difficult the journey might be after our loved one's death. You may ask if it's even possible to prevent grief from consuming us. And the answer is: yes! Please take a deep breath and relax as we analyze effective strategies to help you cope better with your loved one's death.

- **Be Honest with Yourself and Acknowledge Your Feelings.**

The grief you experience after the death of your loved one manifests in stages, and each stage has its own set of feelings. No matter what those feelings are, you shouldn't try to deny or suppress them. For instance, the first feeling that may hit you after your doctor announces your loved one's death is a sense of sorrow but relief at the same time. This doesn't mean you are glad or happy that your loved one has passed. But you are now free to return to your everyday lifestyle. Along with that relief comes the feeling of guilt, and you tell yourself: "Oh, I shouldn't feel relief but sadness." As such, you quickly suppress your relief and allow sadness to dominate in a way to get rid of your guilt. Sometimes, you might hide your sadness altogether to avoid appearing vulnerable to others. However, denying or suppressing your feelings causes more harm than good to your emotional state, for those suppressed feelings will overwhelm you in no time, thus pushing you into depression. You must be honest about your feelings to ensure that this never happens. Remember, feelings are just that, feelings. What's important is what you do with those feelings.

Accept every emotion, no matter how conflicting it might be. Constantly remind yourself that it is okay to feel relieved and sad simultaneously. Don't suppress those healthy emotions because they become an unhealthy cluster of chaos when you do. The best way to start healing is to embrace them honestly and focus on and try to work through them.

- **Don't Compare Your Grieving Process with Those of Your Family Members.**

Our loved one's death affects every family member. However, no two family members experience the same grieving process. How some of them will mourn your loved one's demise will differ significantly from yours because you shared a unique relationship with the deceased, and they have different experiences than yours. For this reason, you must claim your grieving process as a personal journey. Unlike the others, you may experience delayed grieving in which you cannot bring yourself to mourn your loved one until after days or weeks, or after they get buried or cremated. When such happens, don't beat yourself up by saying things like: "I should cry and mourn like others." Instead, recognize that you will deal with this life-changing period in your own way.

Similarly, your grieving process might take much longer than others, or it might be more intense, wherein you not only battle with sadness and grief, but you may feel like you have lost your sense of purpose, without no one to care for any longer. As such, you might find it hard to adjust to a "normal" lifestyle while everybody around you may have moved on with their lives like nothing ever happened. Remember that you took care of this patient for a long time, so you will experience emptiness after their departure.

You need to stay strong and counter negative thoughts by reiterating that you spent most of your daily life with the patient for a long time. For this reason, it's normal that your recovery time be much slower than other family members who barely spend time with the patient. It would be healthier to stop worrying about other family members' grieving journey and instead, focus on your own.

- **Avoid Being Isolated and Lonely.**

When you are grieving over the death of a loved one who means so much to you, it is customary to want to be alone and mourn in your private space. However, it would be best not to allow that need to push you to isolate yourself from other family members, and friends. Such extreme forms of isolation make you lonely, with nothing to distract you temporarily from your feelings or to help you walk through them. The more time you spend in your loneliness, the higher the chances of those negative emotions consuming your mind and leading you to depression. In contrast, your healing process speeds up when you push yourself to reach out to your most trusted people. You would remember that in Chapter 8, we emphasized that as a primary caregiver, you need someone or a group of people who will always be there to offer you emotional support by actively listening as you express your feelings and emotions regarding your caregiving journey. Although your loved one's death marks the end of your caregiving journey, such people can still be a significant source of emotional support.

The fact that they have been with you since the beginning or middle of your caregiving journey makes it easier for you to open up to them and pour out your feelings without fearing getting judged or mocked. As we also mentioned, such people could be anyone, as long as you trust and feel comfortable with them.

- **Join a Support Group for Surviving Family Members or Caregivers of Dementia Patients.**

We already examined how joining a support group as you progress through your caregiving journey can make it easier for you. The same applies in this case, but it would be best if you specifically look for a support group with members who are also surviving caregivers and family members of dementia patients. At first, it might be challenging for you to open up to the group because most of them are probably strangers. However, when you hear their stories of how they lost their loved ones, the challenges before and after their loved ones' deaths, and how they dealt with those challenges, you become filled with a sense of belonging as you quickly picked similarities between their stories and yours. You will become more comfortable sharing your experiences, struggles, and dilemmas. These people who easily understand you will not only listen actively and offer you soothing words of comfort but also give you suggestions based on their experiences.

Note that not everybody you encounter will be emphatic about your recovery from the loved one's death. Often, you will discover people who will make insensitive comments or mockery of your feelings and mental condition. However, such insensitivity often stems from their ignorance. Thus, when such people try to attack or make a mockery of your situation, you can either choose to educate them as to why what they said was wrong and how they can do better, or you can ignore them completely, thus denying them the joy of seeing their actions or words affecting you.

- **Open Up to Your Old Hobbies and Interests or Pick Up New Ones.**

Engaging deeply in self-care is a great coping mechanism you should take advantage of after your loved one's demise. You no longer have to supervise anyone for over fifteen hours a day. You have nothing holding you back from reconnecting with those hobbies and areas of interest you set aside the moment you assumed the role of a dementia caregiver. Whether it be exercising, yoga, hanging out with friends, solo or group traveling, dancing, etc., try to go back to those activities and see if you can rekindle the excitement and satisfaction you used to derive from them. Of course, nothing is wrong if you discover that you no longer enjoy them. It just means that you must search for a new fun activity that can excite you and give you something to look forward to. When you finally find that new hobby or rekindle your love for your old ones, don't hesitate to go for it and have fun because you deserve it!

- **Embrace the Fact that Accepting Your Loved One's Death is a Gradual Process and Not an Automatic Development.**

Grief over a loved one's death is not something that you can solve by crying for long hours on a particular day. Nobody ever deals with the feeling of loss once and gets over it. More often than usual, you will constantly struggle with feelings of loss, especially when you step into their old room or come across your loved one's belongings. However, the intensity of those painful feelings and sense of loss gradually reduces as time passes and you open up to share your feelings with your most trusted people.

I assure you that a time will come when seeing your loved one's belongings will not push you to cry bitterly but to smile and experience gratitude on their behalf. Instead of focusing on your loss, those items will remind you of the beautiful memories you shared throughout your caregiving journey. You might even get encouraged to do things that can keep the memories of your loved one alive for as long as possible. For example, you could plant a tree in your backyard and name it after your loved one. Or you could organize an annual memorial service to celebrate their lives and the remarkable achievements they shared with the world.

Trying to erase your mind and the physical surroundings of your loved one's memory is one of the worst ways to handle or cope effectively with their death. Because you loved and cared for this person so much, you will never succeed at erasing their memories. And occasionally, they will pop up as you do your daily activity until you can no longer control them from awakening unwanted emotions within you. So think about it, isn't it better and more effective to confront your feelings honestly, right from the beginning? Of course, it is! The earlier you take the first step, the closer you will get to that peak point of healing where your loved one's death is no longer a trauma but a trigger to positive memories and feelings such as gratitude, fulfillment, and joy.

To wrap up this chapter, here is a list of some of the online caregiver support groups and online resources to help you navigate your loved one's end-of-life care while providing additional tips to cope better with their death.

SUPPORT GROUPS

- Alzheimer's Association Support Group for Caregivers

- Anam Cara Community

- Wyoming Dementia Together

- ALZConnected Online Community

- The Alzheimer's Foundation of America (AFA)

- Dementia Mentors

BOOK RESOURCES

- Surviving Alzheimer's Practical Tips and Soul-Saving Wisdom for Caregivers by Paul Scott

- The Grace in Dying by Kathleen Dowling Singh

- No Pressure No Diamond: Mining for Gift in Illness and Loss by Teri Dillion

- Being Mortal: Medicine and What Matters at the End by Atul Gawande

ONLINE DOCUMENTARIES AND RESOURCES

- Griefwalker by Time Wilson

- Better Your Goodbyes, developed by Liz Lighter

- My End-of-Life Decisions: An Advance Planning Guide and Toolkit, developed by Compassion and Choices.

CONCLUSION

 "The simple act of caring is heroic."

— Edward Albert

For most caregivers who jump right into the job without prior training and experience, our idea of a successful caregiving journey has always centered on committing fully to our loved one's care while sacrificing our needs and self-care. However, based on the information we have explored throughout the ten chapters of this book, you would agree that the actual key to surviving and succeeding through the inevitable challenges of the caregiving world lies in your ability to treat your needs with the same level of priority and care as those of your dementia loved one. Before we continue, let's briefly recap our journey through each chapter.

We started by analyzing the circumstances that could lead you to assume the role of caregiver and how your caregiving journey will play out at the early onset stage in terms of your duties, the qualities you need to become an excellent caregiver, the ups and downs of caregiving and the likely changes you will notice in your loved one at that stage.

Having set that foundation, we went further to create vivid pictures of the life changes – social, physical, emotional, and mental you should expect to experience as your loved one's dementia condition progresses. Next, we analyzed the seven stages of dementia and how you, as a caregiver, can prepare yourself to handle the symptoms your loved one will likely develop at each stage.

In Chapter 3, we shifted our attention from your caregiving roles to *you* as the primary caregiver. We did an in-depth study of 16 common signs that can quickly tell you if you are suffering from caregiver stress syndrome and burnout. Although discovering these signs quite early has a lot of advantages, it is not enough. Therefore, we also examined some practical strategies you can incorporate into your daily life to overcome those burnout symptoms. Immediately afterward, you learned about physical, emotional, and mental caregiving resilience. These three valuable and powerful assets can help ensure you deliver the best care to your loved one without being overwhelmed by the *emotional* and *psychological* burden of caregiving. Based on our discussion, these three resilience types contribute significantly to ensuring the proper and healthy functioning of a caregiver's body, mind, and soul. We also explored how you can overcome the inevitable daily challenges and behavioral symptoms that become severe obstacles while you are caring for your loved one. Then, we examined what it means to seek help during your caregiving journey, why you need to do it, how to ask for help and get favorable responses, and most importantly, the steps to building an effective caregiving support squad.

Finally, in the last two chapters, we concentrated on how you can make your loved one's end-of-life care as meaningful and less challenging as possible. To do so, we focused on financial and legal planning, which is undoubtedly the most complicated part of caregiving for most of us. We then broke down the complex process into simple steps to enable you to understand it better. We also analyzed the functions of the legal documents in planning for your dementia loved one and how you can set up those documents within any state in the U. S.

We then focused on the steps to caring for your loved one at their critical end stage. In that ultimate chapter, we examined the need for hospice care for their end-of-life care and the appropriate moment to sign them up for it. We also explained how you could ensure that your loved one's wishes and spiritual beliefs get honored and respected in every decision concerning their medical care, finances, and funeral or memorial service. Finally, we wrapped up our discussion by examining the best coping strategies to incorporate into your daily life after the death of your loved one.

While we cannot deny the fact that each of the ten chapters can offer you a wealth of knowledge regarding the best tips, strategies, and skills to become, not only an excellent caregiver but also a physically and emotionally resilient one, trying to internalize and implement them all at once could leave you feeling overwhelmed right at the beginning of your transformation journey. Thus, it is best to take it one step at a time. For example, you can start with building physical resilience before tackling your emotions, or focus on preparing your loved one's Living Will before jumping into their Power of Attorney or Authority. While those baby steps might seem insignificant at first, you'll realize within a short period that they are just what you need to succeed on this new transformation journey that you are about to begin or continue.

I must also emphasize that despite the life-changing benefits that your newly acquired knowledge and skills will have on your caregiving journey, there will be days when the challenges will get so exhausting that the idea of giving up becomes enticing to you. But please don't. In such challenging moments, it's best to calm down and draw inspiration from the success stories of other caregivers like 26-year-old Rachel Smith, who, despite being the youngest in her extended family, assumed the father's primary caregiver role. Although it was pretty tough initially, Rachel kept educating herself about her father's dementia condition and what her role as a caregiver involved. With that knowledge, she eventually balanced between providing adequate care for her father and prioritizing her personal needs. Today, Rachel navigates through the daily challenges her father's condition poses with a positive mentality and gratitude that she gets to spend time with her dad, as the two of them occasionally share stories and conversations. And the best part is that she actually enjoys every moment of it, for it transports her to the times before her father got diagnosed with dementia. Despite his condition, she even has high hopes that her father will be able to walk her down the aisle someday. Isn't that beautiful? Like Rachel, you deserve to experience a less challenging, positive, peaceful, and fulfilling caregiving journey. Your role as a caregiver should not feel like a burden but *a blessing*!

You have now all the necessary tools to make that transformation happen in your caregiving journey. It all begins with resetting your mindset that your self-care is equally as important as your loved ones. Thus, you should invest so much in it, for by doing so, you are indirectly helping your loved one get the best quality care. With that mindset, it becomes much easier to implement the skills, tips, and strategies you have learned into your daily routine and caregiving journey.

I am confident that with time, you will become a physically, mentally, and emotionally resilient caregiver who is not overwhelmed with negative emotions. Instead, just like Rachel, you will bask in calmness, satisfaction, gratitude, happiness, and fulfillment. But until then, I wish you the best of luck from the deepest part of my heart!

FOREWORD BY JOSE G. GARCIA, MD.

JANET G. CRUZ

THE
DEMENTIA
CAREGIVER'S
SURVIVAL GUIDE

An 11-Step Plan to Understand The Disease and How
To Cope with Financial Challenges, Patient Aggression, and
Depression Without Guilt, Overwhelm, or Burnout

ABOUT THE AUTHOR

Janet G. Cruz

Janet is the author of: *The Dementia Caregiver's Guide: An 11-Step Plan to Understand the Disease and How to Cope with Financial Challenges, Patient Aggression, and Depression Without Guilt, Overwhelm, or Burnout.*

She studied Sociology, Psychology, and Fine Arts and expresses her creativity through writing and visual arts. She started writing and publishing her work to process her feelings after losing her husband to cancer. Helping others is a priority for her. She believes life is wonderful despite our many trials.

Through her series of books, she wants to help as many readers as possible by sharing her experiences, knowledge, and thorough research of dementia caregiving so that other caregivers can have a better quality of life as well.

She was the primary caregiver to several family members (her mother, aunt, and husband) for many years, and she is currently the primary caregiver to her father who also suffers from Alzheimer's disease. In this book, the author wanted to address the caregiver's emotional, and physiological challenges of dementia caregiving.

Janet can be reached at publishing@uconcept.com or via social media:

LEAVE A 1-CLICK REVIEW

Customer Reviews

☆☆☆☆☆ 2

5.0 out of 5 stars ▾

5 star		100%
4 star		0%
3 star		0%
2 star		0%
1 star		0%

Share your thoughts with other customers

Write a customer review

See all verified purchase reviews ›

I would be incredibly thankful if you take just
60-seconds to write a brief review on Amazon,
even if it's just a few sentences!

https://amazon.com/review/create-review?asin=B0C4JX3KBF

BIBLIOGRAPHY

AARP. (2011). Create Your Caregiving Team. Retrieved From.
https://www.aarp.org/caregiving/basics/info-2017/create-a-team.html
Alzheimer's Association. (2022). End-of-Life Planning. Retrieved From.
https://www.alz.org/help-support/i-have-alz/plan-for-your-future/end_of_life_
    planning
Alzheimer's Association. (2022). Grief and Loss as Alzheimer's Progresses.
    Retrieved From.
https://www.alz.org/help-support/caregiving/caregiver-health/grief-loss-as-
    alzheimers-progresses
Alzheimer Society. (2021). Anxiety and Agitation. Retrieved From.
https://www.alz.org/help-support/caregiving/stages-behaviors/anxiety-agita
    tion
Alzheimer Society. (2021). Making decisions about end of life care. Retrieved
    From.
https://www.alzheimers.org.uk/get-support/help-dementia-care/end-life-care-
    making-decisions
Alzheimer Society. (2021). Managing ambiguous loss and grief. Retrieved From.
https://alzheimer.ca/en/help-support/i-have-friend-or-family-member-who-
    lives-dementia
Alzheimer Society. (2021). Planning for your future. Retrieved From.
https://alzheimer.ca/en/help-support/im-living-dementia/planning-your-
    future
Alzheimer Society. (2023). StillHere – Five Personal Stories. Retrieved From.
https://alzheimer.mb.ca/still-here-five-personal-stories/
Amore Hospice. (2023). Hospice and Palliative Care Eligibility Guidelines.
    Retrieved From.
http://www.amorehospice.net/hospice-care-for-healthcare-professionals/
    hospice-and-palliative-care-eligibility-guidelines
Anam Cara Giving. (2021). Resources for knowledge, wisdom, and support.
    Retrieved From
https://anamcaracaregiving.org/resources
Ball, A. (2018). Unique Challenges Faced by Alzheimer's & Dementia Caregivers.
    Retrieved From.
https://www.google.com/amp/s/www.caringseniorservice.com/blog/chal
    lenges-alzheimers-dementia-caregivers%3fhs_amp=true

Baton Rouge Behavioral Hospital. (2022). Identifying Emotional Triggers and What They Mean. Retrieved From. https://batonrougebehavioral.com/identifying-emotional-triggers-and-what-they-mean/

Bayada Home Health Care. (2019). What is Spiritual Care in Hospice? Retrieved From. https://www.google.com/amp/s/blog.bayada.com/be-healthy/what-is-spiritual-care-in-hospice%3fhs_amp=true

Berger, B. (2022). How To Make A Dementia Sensory Room. Retrieved From. https://alzheimersweekly.com/2022/04/how-to-make-dementia-sensory-room.html

Bursack, C., B. (2021). Humor shared among caregivers is therapeutic. Retrieved From. https://www.google.com/amp/s/www.agingcare.com/articles/amp/157394

California Courts. (2023). Self-Help Guide: How to become a guardian. Retrieved From. https://selfhelp.courts.ca.gov/guardianship/process

Caring Across Generations. (2014). Caregivers tell us what they need most. Retrieved From. https://caringacross.org/blog/caregivers-tell-us-what-they-need-most/

Carol. (2021). What do caregivers need most? Retrieved From. https://familycaregiversonline.net/what-do-caregivers-need-most/

Colgan, D. (2021). When and How To Say "No" to Caregiving. Retrieved From. https://www.google.com/amp/s/caregiver.com/api/amp/articles/when-to-say-no/

Collier, S. (2021). What's the best way to manage agitation related to dementia? Retrieved From. https://www.health.harvard.edu/blog/whats-the-best-way-to-manage-agitation-related-to-dementia-2020021418816

Craig, S. (2021). Helpful Daily Activities for Dementia Patients: 50 Expert Tips and Suggestions to Keep Your Loved One Engaged. Retrieved From. https://www.seniorlink.com/blog/helpful-daily-activities-for-dementia-patients-50-expert-tips-and-suggestions-to-keep-your-loved-one-engaged

Crossroads Hospice. (2023). Signs of Dying in the Elderly with Dementia. Retrieved From. https://www.crossroadshospice.com/hospice-resources/end-of-life-signs/dementia/

Crumpler, C. (2022). 7 Steps to Being More Mindful. Retrieved From. https://psychcentral.com/blog/how-to-become-a-more-mindful-person

Cuncic, A. (2022). What Does It Mean to Be 'Triggered'. Retrieved From. https://www.verywellmind.com/what-does-it-mean-to-be-triggered-4175432

Dampsey, K. (2022). How To Stop Being So Emotionally Reactive. Retrieved From.

https://theawarenesscentre.com/how-to-stop-being-so-emotionally-reactive/

Davis, J. (2020). 4 Tips to Effectively Ask for Help—and Get a Yes. Retrieved From.

https://www.google.com/amp/s/www.psychologytoday.com/us/blog/tracking-wonder/202002/4-tips-effectively-ask-help-and-get-yes%3famp

Dementia Australia. (2021). Restless behavior in the afternoon. Retrieved From.

https://www.dementia.org.au/about-dementia/carers/behaviour-changes/restless-behaviour-in-the-afternoon

Dementia Australia. (2021). Wandering. Retrieved From.

https://www.dementia.org.au/national/support-and-services/carers/behaviour-changes/wandering

Department of Health. (2015). Managing behavioral and psychological symptoms of dementia. Retrieved From.

https://www.health.vic.gov.au/patient-care/managing-behavioural-and-psychological-symptoms-of-dementia

Derpersio, G. (2022). Revocable Trust vs. Irrevocable Trust: What's the Difference? Retrieved From.

https://www.investopedia.com/ask/answers/071615/what-difference-between-revocable-trust-and-living-trust.asp

DiLonardo, M. J. (2014). When Is It Time to Ask for More Help? Retrieved From.

https://www.webmd.com/alzheimers/features/time-to-ask-for-help

Erickson, L. V. (2021). 4 Differences Between Revocable vs. Irrevocable Trusts. Retrieved From.

https://www.google.com/amp/s/www.racinelaw.net/amp/4-differences-between-revocable-vs-irrevocable-trusts.html

Experia USA. (2021). Sensory Rooms for Dementia. Retrieved From.

https://www.experia-usa.com/blog/alzheimers/sensory-rooms-for-dementia/

Experia USA. (2022). The Best Indoor Sensory Activities for Dementia. Retrieved From.

https://www.experia.co.uk/blog/the-best-indoor-sensory-activities-for-dementia/

First in Care. (2014). Effective Ways to Build a Caregiving Team. Retrieved From.

https://www.firstincare.com/caregiver-wellness-tips/effective-ways-to-build-a-caregiving-team/

Freewill. (2023). Revocable trust vs. irrevocable trust: Key differences and which is right for you. Retrieved From.

https://www.freewill.com/learn/revocable-trust-vs-irrevocable-trust

Hayes, A. (2022). Power of Attorney (POA): Meaning, Types, and How and Why to Set One Up. Retrieved From.

https://www.investopedia.com/terms/p/powerofattorney.asp

Heerema, E. (2022). Responding to Agitation in Dementia. Retrieved From. https://www.verywellhealth.com/tips-on-responding-to-agitation-in-dementia-97642

Hiliger, Z. (2022). Keeping Your Sense of Humor as a Family Caregiver. Retrieved From. https://familycaregiversonline.net/keeping-your-sense-of-humor-as-a-family-caregiver/

Home Care Assistance. (2020). Top 6 Things Family Caregivers Need. Retrieved From. https://www.google.com/amp/s/www.homecareassistancetucson.com/essential-needs-of-a-family-caregiver/amp/

Hospice Care Options. (2021) Is It Time To Call Hospice For Dementia? Retrieved From. https://hcoga.com/blog/is-it-time-to-call-hospice-for-dementia/

Hospital News Canada. (2023). Activities and games for patients with Alzheimer's disease. Retrieved From. https://hospitalnews.com/activities-and-games-for-patients-with-alzheimers-disease/

International End of Life Doula Association. (2023). Caring For The Dying Dementia Patient, Honoring The Person Inside. Retrieved from. https://inelda.org/caring-for-the-dying-dementia-patient-honoring-the-person-inside/

Jahn, M. (2021). Notarization. Retrieved From. https://www.investopedia.com/terms/n/notarize.asp

JustGreatLawyers. (2021). Legal Planning for Dementia and Alzheimer's: A Comprehensive Guide for Patients and Their Families. Retrieved From. https://www.justgreatlawyers.com/legal-planning-dementia-alzheimers

Lim, C. (2021). 20 Simple Things You Can Do Daily To Become a Mindful Person. Retrieved From. https://www.lifehack.org/305575/20-simple-things-you-can-daily-become-mindful-person

Linberg, S. & Weiss, K. (2022). 22 Ways to Calm Yourself Down. Retrieved From. https://www.healthline.com/health/how-to-calm-down

Manhattan MentalJealth Counselling. (2022). What Is Emotional Reactivity And How To End The Cycle. Retrieved From. https://manhattanmentalhealthcounseling.com/what-is-emotional-reactivity-and-how-to-end-the-cycle/

Mayo Clinic Staff. (2021). Alzheimer's and dementia care: Tips for daily tasks. Retrieved From. https://www.mayoclinic.org/healthy-lifestyle/caregivers/in-depth/alzheimers-caregiver/art-20047577

Mayo Clinic Staff. (2022). Living wills and advance directives for medical decisions. Retrieved From.
https://www.mayoclinic.org/healthy-lifestyle/consumer-health/in-depth/living-wills/art-20046303

Morrow, A. (2020). Advantages and Disadvantages of Hospice Care. Retrieved From.
https://www.verywellhealth.com/pros-and-cons-of-hospice-care-1132299

Murphy, A. (2022). How To Stop Being Emotionally Reactive: 13 Techniques That Work. Retrieved From
https://declutterthemind.com/blog/stop-being-emotionally-reactive/

National Institute on Aging. (2017). Tips for Coping with Sundowning. Retrieved From.
https://www.nia.nih.gov/health/tips-coping-sundowning

National Institute on Aging. (2022). Legal and Financial Planning for People with Dementia. Retrieved From.
https://www.nia.nih.gov/health/legal-and-financial-planning-people-alzheimers

National Institute on Aging. (2022). Planning for the Future after a Dementia Diagnosis. Retrieved From.
https://www.alzheimers.gov/life-with-dementia/planning-for-future

National Institute on Aging. (2022). What Are Palliative Care and Hospice Care? Retrieved From.
https://www.nia.nih.gov/health/what-are-palliative-care-and-hospice-care

Naumburg, C. (2022). 6 Simple Steps to Being More Mindful. Retrieved From.
https://www.seleni.org/advice-support/2018/3/21/6-simple-steps-to-being-more-mindful

NicoleReed. (2021). Can Someone With Dementia Make a Trust? Retrieved From.
https://rmolawyers.com/can-someone-with-dementia-make-a-trust/

NHS. (2022). Communicating with someone with dementia. Retrieved From.
https://www.nhs.uk/conditions/dementia/communication-and-dementia/

NHS. (2022). Managing legal affairs for someone with dementia. Retrieved From.
https://www.nhs.uk/conditions/dementia/legal-issues/

Norton Basu LLP. (2020). Using a Revocable Living Trust to Prepare for Assisted Living and Dementia. Retrieved From.
https://www.nortonbasu.com/blog/2020/09/revocable-living-trust-assisted-living-dementia/

Norris, J. (2022). Music therapy improves well-being in people with dementia and caregivers. Retrieved From.
https://www.medicalnewstoday.com/articles/music-therapy-improves-well-being-in-people-with-dementia-and-caregivers

Nurse Partners. (2020). Responding to Pacing Behavior in Dementia. Retrieved From.

https://www.nursepartners.org/responding-pacing-behavior-dementia/

Nunez, K. (2020). The Benefits of Guided Imagery and How To Do It. Retrieved From.

https://www.healthline.com/health/guided-imagery

Palmer, J., Hilgeman, M., Balboni, T., Paasche-orlow, & Sullivan, J. (2021). The Spiritual Experience of Dementia From the Health Care Provider Perspective: Implications for Intervention. Retrieved From.

https://academic.oup.com/gerontologist/article/62/4/556/6366348

Psychological Health Care. (2017). How to Keep Calm Under Pressure. Retrieved From.

https://www.psychologicalhealthcare.com.au/blog/keep-calm-pressure/

Tedeschi, B. (2016). How do you honor a dementia patient's end-of-life-wishes? Retrieved from.

https://www.statnews.com/2016/08/26/dementia-alzeheimer-end-of-life/

Raphan, M. S. (2022). Guardianship & Conservatorships. Retrieved From.

https://alzfdn.org/guardianship-conservatorships/

Schiltz, R. (2023). Pros And Cons Of Hospice. Retrieved from.

https://seniorsafetyadvice.com/pros-and-cons-of-hospice/

Schiltz, R. (2023). What Do Caregivers Need Most? Retrieved From.

https://seniorsafetyadvice.com/what-do-caregivers-need-most/

Scott, H. (2016). The importance of spirituality for people living with dementia. Retrieved From.

https://pubmed.ncbi.nlm.nih.gov/26884040/

Shega, J. (2023). Hospice Eligibility Guidelines. Retrieved From.

https://www.vitas.com/for-healthcare-professionals/hospice-and-palliative-care-eligibility

Shelley. (2019). 4 Repetitive Tasks That Help Decrease Alzheimer's Agitation. Retrieved From.

https://www.google.com/amp/s/www.heritageseniorcommunities.com/4-repetitive-tasks-that-help-decrease-alzheimers-agitation/amp/

Shortsleeve, C. (2022). Asking for Help Is So Damn Hard. Here's How to Make It Easier. Retrieved From.

https://www.google.com/amp/s/www.self.com/story/how-to-ask-for-help/amp

Smith, M. (2022). What's the Difference Between Palliative Care and Hospice Care. Retrieved From.

https://www.webmd.com/palliative-care/difference-palliative-hospice-care

The Reutlinger Community. (2021). Dealing with Loss and Bereavement. Retrieved From https://www.rcjl.org/dementia-grief-loss-adjusting-after-bereavement-part-4-of-4/

Stringfellow, A. (2019). Activities for Dementia Patients: 50 Tips and Ideas to Keep Patients with Dementia Engaged. Retrieved From.
https://www.seniorlink.com/blog/activities-for-dementia-patients-50-tips-and-ideas-to-keep-patients-with-dementia-engaged

Vitas Healthcare. (2022). Hospice Care for Alzheimer's Disease and Dementia. Retrieved from.
https://www.vitas.com/care-services/personalized-care-plans-by-diagnosis/alzheimers-disease-and-dementia

Vitas Healthcare. (2022). What are the Differences and Commonalities Between Hospice and Palliative Care? Retrieved From.
https://www.vitas.com/hospice-and-palliative-care-basics/about-palliative-care/hospice-vs-palliative-care-whats-the-difference

WebMD Editorial Contributors. (2022). Alzheimer's Disease and Care at the End of Life. Retrieved from.
https://www.webmd.com/alzheimers/alzheimers-hospice-end-of-life-care

Wilson, P. (2020). Tired of Caring? Why Saying No To Caregiving is Easier Than You Think. Retrieved From.
https://pameladwilson.com/tired-of-caring-why-saying-no-to-caregiving-is-easier-than-you-think-caring-for-aging-parents-blog/

Wynn, P. (2019). How to Improve Fine Motor Skills Affected by Neurologic Disorders. Retrieved From.
https://www.brainandlife.org/articles/a-loss-of-fine-motor-skills-is-a-common-symptom

Tia Walker Quote. Retrieve From.
https://www.nursehomecare.ca/site/blog/2018/07/10/homecare-services-inspirational-quotes-for-dementia-caregivers

Lao Tzu Quote. Retrieve From.
https://parade.com/1004993/marynliles/caregiver-quotes/

Iris Proverb Quote. Retrieve From.
Quotes for Dementia Caregivers in Need of Inspiration | ActivePro Nursing & Homecare Inc. | Niagara (nursehomecare.ca)

Carey Mulligan Quote. Retrieve From.
Quotes for Dementia Caregivers in Need of Inspiration | ActivePro Nursing & Homecare Inc. | Niagara (nursehomecare.ca)

Alfred North Whitehead Quote. Retrieve From.
Alfred North Whitehead - No one who achieves success does... (brainyquote.com)

Brian Clough Quote. Retrieve From.
https://www.brainyquote.com/quotes/brian_clough_181427

Edward Albert Quote. Retrieve From.

https://parade.com/1004993/marynliles/caregiver-quotes/
Amy Leigh Mercree Quote. Retrieve From.
https://www.caringbridge.org/resources/inspirational-quotes-on-caregiving/?
gclid=EAIaIQobChMIpa7644DN_gIVABOzAB1yoQcHEAAYAiAAEgKwl
PD_BwE&gclsrc=aw.ds
Les Brown Quote. Retrieve From.
https://www.caringbridge.org/resources/inspirational-quotes-on-caregiving/?
gclid=EAIaIQobChMIpa7644DN_gIVABOzAB1yoQcHEAAYAiAAEgKwl
PD_BwE&gclsrc=aw.ds
Amy A. Quote. Retrieve From.
https://www.caringbridge.org/resources/inspirational-quotes-on-caregiving/?
gclid=EAIaIQobChMIpa7644DN_gIVABOzAB1yoQcHEAAYAiAAEgKwl
PD_BwE&gclsrc=aw.ds
Active Pro, Nursing and HomeCare, Inc. Quote. Retrieve From.
https://www.nursehomecare.ca/site/blog/2018/07/10/homecare-services-inspi
rational-quotes-for-dementia-caregivers